Publication of this book has been
assisted by support from
Clarks Shoes, Street

Birds of
SOMERSE

Birds of
SOMERSET

SOMERSET ORNITHOLOGICAL SOCIETY

ALAN SUTTON
1988

ALAN SUTTON PUBLISHING
BRUNSWICK ROAD · GLOUCESTER

First published 1988

British Library Cataloguing in Publication Data

Somerset Ornithological Society.
Birds of Somerset.
1. Somerset. Birds
I. Title
598.29423'8

ISBN 0-86299-471-3

*Jacket illustrations: Background, Wigeon over Tealham Moor. Foreground,
Redshank, Tealham Moor – Robin Williams.*

Typesetting and origination by
Alan Sutton Publishing Limiting.
Printed in Great Britain by
WBC Print Ltd.

Contents

Foreword

This is the first book on this subject since 1968, and it owes its inspiration to members of the Editorial Committee for the *Report on Somerset Birds*, who agreed in 1986 that a new work should be written. In the last twenty years there have been many changes together with a great accumulation of records and knowledge.

The book is essentially a compilation from the records of members and others published in the *Report*. Space has unfortunately not allowed us to acknowledge individual records, as we should have liked to have done. Most of the book was compiled by seven members of the Committee: D.K. Ballance, T.A. Box, A.J. Bundy, D.J. Chown, B.J. Hill, D.E. Paull and B.E. Slade.

They also contributed to the Introduction, as did the following members of the Society: D.H.Thompson (Holcombe and Coleford); J.A. McGeoch (Lower Brue Valley); J.A. Humphrey (West Sedge Moor); J.V. Chidgey (Quantocks); A.J. Parsons (Crewkerne); R.J. Butcher (Wimbleball Lake); N.V. Allen (Exmoor).

The tasks were co-ordinated by A.J. Parsons, the current President of the Society. Special thanks are due to Robin Williams for the cover illustrations, to Terry Box for the county Map, and his effort in putting the manuscript on to floppy disk, and to David Ballance for invaluable guidance and patient correction of the drafts.

We are most grateful to those who provided help with the illustrations: T.A. Box, Brian, Andrew and David Slade, Simon White (of West Air Photography, Weston-super-Mare), R.P.A.F. Williams and G.H.E. Young.

The drawings are the work of: T.A. Box, D.E. Paull and B.E. Slade.

We are indebted to many members of the Society and others for their observations over the last twenty years, and for their assistance in the preparation of the book. Among these are: P.G. Akers, P.A. Amies, R.

Angles, C.F.S. Avent, S.S.B. Ball, R.P. Ballantine, P.P. Betts, F.W. Board, R.C. Branwhite, D.L. Buckingham, B. Carter, P.J. Chadwick, the late G.M. Chadwyck-Healey, S.E. Chapman, the late G.E. Clothier, H.J. Craske, R.M. Curber, A.H. Davis, the late H.H. Davis, P.R.K. Davis, C.F. Dibble, S.H. Durston, S.B. Edwards, D.R. Eele, A.W. Evans, D.S. Evans, K.L. Fox, P.L. Garvey, B.D. Gibbs, M.A. Hallett, R.S. Harkness, G.F.G. Harper, R.C.F. Hastings, T.G. Hiscock, J.G. Hole, S.C. Holland, the late E.G. Holt, M.J. Hudson, M.J. Ingram, M. Kendall, J.G. Keylock, the late B. King, D.E. Ladhams, H.R.H. Lance, C.G. Manning, B.J. Mathews, D.F. Miller, J.V. Morley, R.B. Ninnes, E.M. Palmer, P.R. Pearce, G. Pell-Walpole, the late D.H. Perrett, R.J. Prytherch, B. Rabbitts, K. Rosenau, J.B.O. Rossetti, the late W.L. Roseveare, the late R. Ryall, E.M. Seaman, T.B. Silcocks, A.M. Slade, N.R. Smith, H.C. Squire, E.P. Stephens, G. Suter, G. Sweet, B. Taylor, S.M. Taylor, J.V. Towler, K.E. Vinicombe, D. Warden, W.J. Webber, B.J. Widden, E.M. Williams, M.G. Wilson, M.A. Wright, K.B. Young, G.H.E. Young.

General Introduction

The last book on this subject was Palmer and Ballance's *The Birds of Somerset* (1968) which summarised records from the earliest times to 1965, with a few notable ones for 1966.

Since then, the status of many species has changed greatly, and there has been an accumulation of evidence on their distribution. But the county has changed, too. From Saxon times down to 1974, its boundaries had remained almost unaltered, apart from a few adjustments along the south and south-west borders and encroachments by Bristol. The creation of the new county of Avon removed about 16 per cent of the area of Somerset, including the two largest towns, Bath and Weston-super-Mare. From the ornithological standpoint, the greatest losses were Chew Valley and Blagdon Lakes, with Weston Bay, Sand Bay, Sand Point, and the island of Steep Holm. The bulk of the Mendip Hills remained within Somerset, except the north slopes and the western outlier of Bleadon Hill. Although the *Report on Somerset Birds* continued to record the birds of south Avon until 1977, this book deals only with the birds of the 'new' county.

With an area of 345,094ha, this is now 16th in size among the 39 counties of England. Its rural nature is well shown by the fact that it is 35th in population; among southern counties, only Cornwall and the Isle of Wight have fewer than its 450,800 people.

The essential crescent shape of the county still remains, its centre formed by the alluvial plain of the Rivers Axe, Brue and Parrett. This was once flooded by the sea, and its history has been a long struggle against tide and flood. It is broken up by ridges and islands, of which the most conspicuous are the Polden Hills, Brent Knoll and Glastonbury Tor. The alluvial deposits lie partly on a bed of blue lias, which stretches south-east from Bridgwater to the Penselwood Ridge along the Wiltshire border, and from there south-west to the Blackdown Hills. The levels south of the Poldens, the Vale of Taunton and the coastal lowlands of the west lie chiefly on the Keuper marls. In places, there is a layer of peat above the clay, especially in the area immediately west of Glastonbury, where it is commercially exploited.

To the north, the plain is bordered by the limestone ridge of the Mendip Hills, once famous for its mines and still for its caves and quarries; these run from Frome to Brean Down on the coast.

The semicircle of hills along the Wiltshire and Dorset borders, from east of Frome to Crewkerne, is mainly formed by the south-west end of the oolite limestones, which give the noble yellow tone to south Somerset villages. However, the hills between Crewkerne and Chard, and the Blackdown ridge to the west, are of upper greensand, capped by chalk east and west of Chard. The western part of the county, from the Parrett to the Devon border, and south to the edge of the Vale of Taunton Deane, is of Red Devon sandstone, which forms first the isolated block of the Quantock Hills, and then the high plateau of the Brendon Hills and Exmoor, both deeply indented by wooded combes. The far western part of Exmoor is in Devon.

The last twenty years have witnessed great changes in the Somerset countryside, some of which we have analysed in detail in the articles that follow. Of these, the most obviously disastrous has been the total loss of elm trees. For centuries this had been a dominant tree, especially in south Somerset, and its loss has changed almost beyond recognition the familiar views from, for example, Camel Hill or Ham Hill. This has been coupled with the general tidying-up stemming from intensive farming methods: the disappearance of hedgerow timber, the removal of hedges and of small corners of wilderness, and the now universal practice of mechanical clipping. Rivers have also suffered in the cause of flood-prevention and agriculture: outflows have been straightened, beds scoured, willows and other trees removed. The problems of draining the levels have now largely been solved by more efficient ditching and pumping, so that extensive flooding is less common; much land that was permanent rough pasture has become good grass or even arable, and in most parts the unique landscape of the levels is now only a memory. Tourism has brought increasing disturbance, especially to open land in the west, where pressures are in some places too high and still mounting. Less obvious, yet insidious, have been changes brought about by the acidification of rivers, the use of herbicides and pesticides, and the pollution by agricultural waste products. Yet some human influences on the landscape have been beneficial to birdlife: well-planted suburban gardens are more attractive than treeless prairies; an excellent reservoir, Wimbleball, has enriched the Brendon Hills; and even giant pylons have provided Cormorant roosts!

Moreover, we have seen an enormous growth of interest in nature and its conservation. Many have come to realise that without constant pressure on public and private authorities and the giving and spending of a great deal of money there will be little wildlife left to enjoy. They may not be able to stop the destruction of Madagascar's forests but they can do something nearer to home. There are now 43 reserves in the county owned or managed by the Somerset Naturalists' Trust (of which a number are, admittedly, too small to be of much use to birdlife), and one owned by the Royal Society for the Protection of Birds. Other areas are controlled by the Nature Conservancy Council and by the county Council, or by local natural history groups. We have also seen a start made to schemes of statutory compensation to farmers to prevent intensive development of sensitive sites. Though there have been much-publicised clashes of interest, as over West Sedge Moor, there has been a growing realisation of the possibilities of co-operation between apparently conflicting interests, as on the peat-moors.

Gains and Losses

In the past twenty years, the county has gained five regular breeding birds. Two of these, Fulmar and Cetti's Warbler, have been generally extending their range in north-west Europe. The arrival of Siskin is linked with the spread of coniferous plantation. The Black-tailed Godwit has been honoured by the creation of a special reserve, but it only just survives there. Bearded Tits have recently become established in one area. In addition to these, Peregrines have returned to some old sites, which had been temporarily deserted because of a decrease in the population caused by chemical residues. Three introduced wildfowl, the Greylag and Egyptian Geese and the Mandarin, have bred, and a fourth, the Canada Goose, has greatly extended its range. The Collared Dove, first recorded as breeding in 1964, has now spread widely. Among passerines, Willow Tits have proved more widespread than had been thought, as have the Exmoor Ring Ouzels; Pied Flycatchers have greatly increased in the west, aided in some places by the provision of nestboxes. Marsh Harriers and Firecrests have bred recently, and Goshawks may have done so.

There is a much longer catalogue of losses and decreases. The loss of south Avon removed Cormorant, Ruddy Duck, Pochard and Shoveler from the list of regular breeders (though Gadwall have now spread to the peat-moors), Black Grouse have died out, and Red Grouse, also, may be on the verge of extinction. Corncrakes, Red-backed Shrikes and Woodlarks no longer breed. Cirl Buntings survive, but are greatly reduced. Some summer visitors have suffered from cold springs or dried-out African winters: Turtle Dove, Nightjar, Sand Martin, Nightingale, Redstart and Whitethroat are examples of these. On the levels, drainage has affected several wetland species, especially Snipe and Yellow Wagtail. For recent surveys of the birds of the levels, see Round (1978) and Weaver, Murfitt and Chown (1983). Tree Sparrows are much reduced and it is doubtful whether Hawfinches still breed.

In recent years, much more time has been spent on sea-watching, and it has been shown that a number of seabirds are commoner than they were once thought to be; this is especially true of divers and skuas, and of some rarer gulls. Mist-netting has proved the regularity of Aquatic Warblers.

The current Somerset list is 329 species, of about 350 identifiable forms. Of these, 143 have bred, and about 106 do so regularly; this is compared with 112 regular breeders in 1965.

Birds formerly on the 'Somerset' list that were only recorded for south Avon before 1974 are listed in the Appendix (p. 238).

Habitats

We have asked some contributors to write short articles of special interest. These do not cover the entire county, but are representative of the most rewarding areas, and some more ordinary ones.

The rest of the county has been described in less detail, to indicate highlights and to suggest places that deserve further investigation. There is a lot of unknown territory; the records of a county's birds will always reflect the distribution of the keenest observers.

EAST SOMERSET AND THE MENDIPS

The east has attracted relatively little attention. It is mainly a land of dairy farming and great estates, or their relics, though Frome, once a great cloth-manufacturing centre, was for a time the largest town in Somerset. The eastern end of the Mendips was a place of weaving and mining; today, motorists everywhere drive over the crushed products of its noisy quarries.

The country from Avon south to Wincanton is dominated by parks and the remains of monastic estates along the western edge of the ancient royal hunting forest of Selwood. Of modern estates, only Orchardleigh is easily accessible to the public; here the attractive lake once provided the only Somerset breeding record of the Black-necked Grebe, and the Great Crested Grebe still breeds occasionally. Other parks are at Ammerdown, Farleigh Hungerford, Mells, Marston, and, further south, Redlynch (which sometimes dries out, but has a small reed-bed). All these except Ammerdown have lakes large enough to support a few Coot and duck; there are also ponds at Chantry, Berkley and Witham. The long escarpment of the Wiltshire border, the most marked natural frontier of Somerset, is almost continuously wooded

Marston Bigot

from Roddenbury, east of Frome, south to the A303 at Penselwood; much of this woodland is an overspill from the great Wiltshire estates of Longleat, Maiden Bradley and Stourhead. This is the only place in Somerset where Woodcock breed at all regularly. Crossbills occur, and have bred. Goldcrests and Tree Pipits are widespread, there are sometimes Nightjars and Wood Warblers, and Willow Tits are probably resident. There are other large woodlands away from the ridge: Postlebury Wood has produced Nightjars in the past, and so, more recently, has Witham Park. Grey Wagtails breed on many streams, and Dippers here and there, mostly to the west of Frome. The small Kingfisher population has been much affected by cold winters. Buzzards and Sparrowhawks breed over most of the area.

Much of the east is very under-watched, but the area around Holcombe and Coleford has received some attention in recent years.

HOLCOMBE AND COLEFORD

The Mells River Valley which runs to the south of Holcombe and Coleford is a well-wooded area on the extreme southern edge of the old coalfield, with the Mendip limestone rising on the far side of the river. Ash, oak, birch and alder are the dominant trees. The farms are almost wholly pastoral; the fields are small and few are cultivated. Consequently, Lapwing are scarce and Partridges almost unknown, but all the common woodland species are here: the three woodpeckers, Nuthatches in abundance, Treecreepers, Goldcrests and tits. The uncommon Willow Tit has been known to breed and Tree Sparrows may also be found.

The river has Dippers, nesting usually under the bridges, and breeding Kingfishers and Grey Wagtails. The Grey Heron is a frequent visitor. Of the birds of prey, Sparrowhawks are more numerous than Kestrels, Buzzards are regular, and Hobbies appear to be breeding in the area. Several recent sightings of Goshawks in an area with so much woodland are of interest.

Little of the woodland has scrubby under-storey suitable for species such as Nightingales and Garden Warblers, but both have bred recently. Blackcaps are common, and Whitethroats are usually outnumbered by Lesser Whitethroats. Wood Warblers and Tree Pipits occur only as passage-migrants, as do Redstarts, Pied Flycatchers, Wheatears and Ring Ouzels. Siskins and Redpolls visit the alders and birches in most winters, and Woodcock appear when it is very cold. A pair of Little Grebes have bred on a secluded pond, and Green Sandpiper and Jack Snipe have been recorded on the ground; other waders such as Greenshank, Dunlin, Curlew and Whimbrel are normally only seen in flight.

Recent sightings of Wryneck, Quail, Merlin, Great Skua and Little Gull indicate the fact that many species cross the country on a broad front and do not simply fly from one bird-ringing station to the next.

Donald Thompson

West of the Fosse Way, and beyond the deep-cut valleys of the Frome's western tributaries, the Mendip plateau develops. It is a straight-roaded land, much of it of fairly recent enclosure. The fields lie over an ancient industrial landscape, the remains of the lead mining for which the Mendips were famous from Roman times till the nineteenth century. In winter, there are large flocks of corvids, and Common Gulls on the grassland. Beech is planted as shelter belts or small copses, and there are two large areas of Forestry Commission conifers, on Stock Hill and Rowberrow Warren. The former has had breeding Redpolls in the past and attracts Crossbills in

Priddy Pools

'invasion' years; Willow Tits are probably regular. Wood Warblers have bred on Eaker Hill and in Mendip Lodge Wood. There is a small lake, at Emborough Pond. Of the old mining areas, Priddy Pools and Charterhouse remain as small breaks of wilderness, as do the Yoxter Rifle Range and the summit of Black Down, the highest point of the Mendips (325m). There were once breeding Black Grouse and Golden Plover; there are still Tree Pipits, a few Whinchats, Redstarts, and Grasshopper Warblers. But the most interesting, though elusive, bird of the open tops is the Corn Bunting, of which there were about twelve pairs around Green Ore in 1986.

The south-west slopes from the Horringtons to Axbridge fall steeply to the levels, and have remained partly uncultivated or wooded. All three woodpeckers occur, as do regular Nuthatches, occasional Willow Tits, and Tree Pipits. Along the base of the slope is the market-gardening area of the Cheddar Valley, once a stronghold of breeding Cirl Buntings. Cheddar Gorge once held Peregrines and Ravens; it may be that a pair or two of the latter do nest somewhere undetected in the west Mendips. Buzzards occur, but have apparently not bred in very recent years west of Wells. Dippers have bred on the Yeo in Cheddar. The cliff and quarry faces attract a large population of Jackdaws. The open ground on the western Mendip outliers (Fry's Hill, Wavering Down and Crook Peak) hold a few Stonechats, and it has been on these limestone slopes, with their faint echo of southern Europe, that small numbers of Red-legged Partridges have maintained themselves since their introduction in 1817. From the limestone caverns beneath the hills has come evidence of the birdlife of Somerset in prehistoric times, when Ptarmigan creaked amongst the snow-covered outcrops.

Between the Mendips and the Poldens lie two parallel tracts of levels. The northernmost is along the the River Axe westward from Wookey. Since the reclamation of Stoke Moor, once a notable Snipe ground, this has been of little interest. Within it, however, between Axbridge and Cheddar, at the foot of the Mendips, is Cheddar Reservoir.

Cheddar Reservoir

CHEDDAR RESERVOIR

Completed in 1937, the reservoir is an almost circular, concrete-banked water, holding 61,425 million litres of water with a surface area of 95.5ha. There are entrances at Cheddar and Axbridge, and a part-tarmaced road offers easy viewing around the entire 3.52km perimeter. At the west end, the water reaches a depth of about 11.6m, but in autumn, when the level drops, concrete shelving and weed-covered sand and gravel islands are exposed, mainly in the northern and eastern sectors.

The reservoir is locally important for wintering wildfowl, particularly diving duck, with up to 1000 Pochard, 800 Tufted Duck, and 100 Goldeneye; at least 2000 Coot are regular. In winter, divers, rarer grebes and Long-tailed Duck occasionally turn up, often staying for long periods.

The round shape, fairly steep concrete banks, and wind-exposed position usually make Cheddar one of the last open waters in the area to freeze, and it regularly attracts birds displaced from Chew Valley and Blagdon on the Avon side of the Mendips.

Sizeable gull roosts develop during the shortest winter months; at other times gulls use the reservoir as a pre-roost washing and feeding stop. Black-headed and Common Gulls are the most numerous, with several hundred Lesser Black-backed Gulls on passage, but the larger gulls are much scarcer since the closure of Axbridge tip in the early 1970s.

Duck numbers dwindle rapidly through March, and waders pass through in small numbers till the end of May; there are consistently high counts of up to 50 Common Sandpipers, and much smaller numbers of Ringed Plovers, Little Ringed Plovers, Dunlin and Sanderling. Good numbers of hirundines can occur, as can flocks of Pied, White and Yellow Wagtails. Terns pass through during April and May, but few stay for any length of time.

The summer months are very quiet. Occasional Common Scoter visit in July, and waders and dabbling duck arrive from early August.

September can be a very exciting time if suitable muddy conditions are available, with passage of the commoner waders and the occasional rarer visitor. Duck numbers, particularly of dabbling duck, build up rapidly. These are mainly replaced by diving duck and Coot as the water level rises, often quite quickly, in October/November.

The reservoir is only some 15km from the coast, and as such is well placed to receive storm-driven seabirds, including occasional skuas, Leach's and Storm Petrels and, almost annually, Grey Phalaropes.

Following a change in Bristol Water Works' maintenance policy, seed-bearing weeds and shrubs now sprout on the concrete banking and shelving as the water level drops, and this offers cover for up to 250 Linnets, and for other finches and pipits, and even a Richard's Pipit and a Wryneck have occurred.

Sailing has perhaps grown in popularity on Wednesday afternoons and at the weekend; the increasing number of windsurfers appear to be less restrained than their yachting companions. Conversely, fewer fishermen use the reservoir, following a decrease in fish numbers due to predation by Pike and to disease. However, discarded tackle remains a problem, with Great Crested Grebes, Coots and even a Shag and a Long-tailed Duck becoming casualties. The introduction of weed-eating Carp has been discussed, to help curb the growth of weed prompted by nutrients seeping into the water supply.

The reservoir is no longer wardened by Bristol Water Works employees, and access is in effect unchecked; joggers have become a regular feature since the late 1970s, and schoolchildren use the reservoir as a short cut between Axbridge and Cheddar. As a result, passerines rarely stay in one place for any length of time, both ducks and waders are subject to much disturbance, and accurate counting is made rather difficult.

Just to the south of the reservoir lie the Cheddar clay-pits. The several adjoining pools, managed by the Cheddar Angling Club, are now less attractive to birds. Much of the *Phragmites* has been removed, and Reed Warblers no longer breed. Small numbers of duck sometimes occur, and have included Goosander, Ruddy Duck and Goldeneye. The most notable records are of a Great Snipe in 1949, and of Cetti's Warblers which raised three young in 1983.

A couple of rough fields either side of the clay-pits are a regular feeding ground for a small flock of Whimbrel in spring.

Terry Box

The Axe Levels are separated from those of the Brue by a low ridge from Wells to Wedmore. The Lower Brue Valley is one of the most interesting areas in Somerset, and is here described in detail.

THE LOWER BRUE VALLEY

This is the low-lying area of peat moorland west of Glastonbury as far as the clay belt, south of the ridge running from Wells to the Isle of Wedmore, and north of the Polden Hills. It is composed mainly of permanent pasture land with a relatively high water table with two areas of raised peat on either side of the Brue: 890ha to the north and 1500ha to the south.

Between 1770 and 1830 all the moors had been enclosed but their drainage was undertaken in an uncoordinated and ineffective way for the rest of the nineteenth century. It was during this period that the ditch system was developed which laid the pattern of field outlines that has persisted to the present day. A certain amount of tree planting was carried out at this time, too, mainly to mark out roads, droves and support banks. Attempts were made to grow corn on some of the reclaimed land but they were mostly unsuccessful, and after some years the land was largely given over to grazing and fattening. Grazing was mostly by cattle; hay was cut and the field ditches were cleared by hand, probably within a three- to five-year cycle. Winter flooding was regular, as the whole system depended on a low river level. The run off via the field ditches and connecting rhynes to drains, thence to the river, was irregular and infrequent in most winters, as so often the river was full of water from run off higher up the valley. This resulted, on occasions, in many moors staying inundated for months at a time. Winter floods, rich in both oxygen and nutrients, softened up the land and released many plant seeds, making them available at the flood line. This whole process not only benefited the wild life of the moors at the time and later on in the year, but helped to maintain the pastures too. Summer floods occurred at times, but they were of a quite different character: being deficient in oxygen they not only washed out ground-nesting birds but ruined the summer grazing and destroyed most of the soil invertebrates.

It was during this period that the breeding birds of the moors as we know them today became established: such wading species as Lapwing, Snipe, Curlew, and Redshank, with some in large numbers in winter. Yellow Wagtails also thrived in the area, and many birds on passage used the moors regularly. The winter floods attracted swans, geese and large numbers of duck as well as the waders, but the breeding avifauna was not quite the same as prior to the enclosures. Then it must have been more associated with a wetter marshland habitat with more close cover than occurs in a field system.

Throughout the rest of the nineteenth century the pastures did not change much: willows were pollarded, ditches cleared by hand, and this new balance was estabilised between man and the wildlife on the moors. This was a period when the rich botanical variety of the area was maintained in and around the field- and ditch-systems.

There was no really new drainage works until well into the twentieth century. In 1942 the Gold Corner Pumping Station was built to pump water from the South Drain into the newly dug Huntspill River and to help clear high water in the Brue by pumping back via the Cripp's River to the Huntspill River. This not only provided more water for the Royal Ordnance

Winter flooding – Tealham Moor

Factory at Puriton but virtually eliminated flooding from this part of the valley south of the river. The North Drain remained unpumped until 1958 when a pumping station was built at the outlet to the river. Only then were the principal drainage schemes for the Lower Brue Valley completed. Then a period of rapid changes came to the valley as a whole, as alongside the fast-changing farming scene, with all its 'improvements', the peat-extraction industry became modernised and highly efficient.

At this point it is worth considering why the moors in their old state were so attractive to so many birds at all seasons. Taking one of the 'specialist' species as a guide and discussing its requirements is a good way to demonstrate why the moors were so favourable for them; then I shall look at the changes that have occurred in the last thirty years and show what has happened, pointing out what could happen in the future. The Snipe is such a bird; several other species have similar requirements. It needs soft organic soils rich in food organisms, principally invertebrates such as various worms, larvae and adult flies, molluscs, crustaceans and amphipods, with a high water table of around 15–20cm in summer, and access to shallow water. It also likes areas of taller vegetation separated by more open ground with low tussocks or clumps of sedge or rush. The old fields as they were provided most of these conditions. The organic soils were soft for most of the year, the high water table kept the soil invertebrates accessible and there was plenty of cover in sedge-beds, rush-clumps, meadow grasses and ditch-margin vege-tation. The shape of the hand-cleared ditch in section is that of a wide shallow V, so there was always shallow water available, which is most important for the young during their early days, with enough cover to conceal them, especially if drier weather was making the field surfaces harder. Grazing produced enough manure to support the soil-invertebrate populations and, as already mentioned, winter floods brought in further nutrients too. Hay-making always began well into the summer, and summer grazing usually started late on the moor proper, due to the ground being too soft in spring. All this considerably reduced the disturbance of breeding birds. Many fields carried superb sedge-beds and others many clumps of rush, just right for day roosts during the non-breeding season and extensive enough to provide cover for the large numbers of winter visitors. So what has happened since the 1950s?

The thinking at that time was for Britain to become more self-sufficient in food, relying less on imports, since we had learnt how vulnerable we became during the 1939–45 war. The farmers were asked to produce more food and they responded magnificently, resulting in a huge reduction in the amount paid for imported food. Subsidies encouraged an intensification of land management, all to improve productivity on the farms and make the country more self-sufficient. The damage to the countryside in general could not be fully forseen. Some parts of the country saw the results before us, such as the loss of hedgerows in East Anglia and the development of enormous field systems with little cover at all. With us the changes were slower and more fragmented, but the first main effect was the ending of the prolonged winter flood and the resulting 'super soak'. The knock-on effect of this was the earlier drying out of the surfaces of the fields in spring, leading to an earlier cultivation, grazing and hence disturbance. To increase stocking rates, fertiliser use was increased to produce an earlier flush of grass, leading again to earlier grazing. Silage making, starting in May, became more frequent, and less hay was made later in the summer. To carry more stock on the same land, new grass strains such as Italian rye were used to reseed some fields and provide more yield per acre. To get a really early start in the spring and extend grazing well into the autumn, some farmers installed pipe drains and their own closed pumping systems. So the combination of rapid drying out in spring, fertilising, reseeding and early grazing soon rendered many fields birdless. The hard surfaces were useless for probing waders and the general disturbance made breeding impossible. Some farmers have in a small way grown corn or potatoes on this drier land but basically the moors are still permanent, albeit drier, pastures. In winter these fields never soften up very much and remain free of flooding except for a few days when the main drains are not pumped out due to a full river. So this development has given us all much more home-produced meat and dairy produce, but we have lost most of our soft-surfaced fields with a high water table and many of our rushy fields and sedge-beds too. The clearing of the ditches, now by machines, many on an annual basis, is producing some field-ditches resembling mini-canals with precious few shallow margins at all, providing far less accessible cover. The prolonged botanical successions in these ditches have gone but the aquatic invertebrates needing more open water are surviving more successfully in the recently-cleared ditches compared with a reduction of species in ditches left for longer periods of up to three years. As a result of all these changes it is not surprising that Snipe and many other species are declining on the moors.

The Somerset Trust for Nature Conservation owns land in seven parts of the valley totalling 138ha. On its permanent pasture reserves such as Tealham Moor, by developing sympathetic ditch-clearing regimes, and by later grazing and mowing, by digging scrapes, penning some ditches, and avoiding artificial fertilising and the use of herbicides, it has managed to provide suitable habitat for many birds throughout the year. This is only a small fraction of the total area of the valley and can only provide a minor refuge in the district as a whole. So what is to become of the pastures in the future? Certain parts of the valley have been designated Sites of Special Scientific Interest, so no further damaging agricultural practices can be carried out, but the main drainage systems are still working to the previously set pattern and the winter floods soon clear away. The summer pen (the water level to which the whole drainage system is set) is still well below what we would like it to be. This must continue to result in earlier drying out of the fields unless these regimes are altered in some way. Here mention must be made of the Environmentally Sensitive Area scheme as well as the SSSI. Payments within the SSSI scheme are made to farmers on an individual farm and field basis, to provide for suitable management that will be friendly to the environment. Within the ESA scheme payments are made at a flat rate per hectare for a certain area as a whole, again for generally managing the land within certain guidelines. This is where it should be possible to organise payments to cover a period of winter flooding in certain parts of the valley and to try and find ways of having a higher summer pen too in specified areas within both these schemes. Payments would have to allow for a restricted summer season. As the valley's wildlife depends on winter flooding, now so much reduced, and on a high summer pen (not a flood), which has been falling during the period under review, it is here, on the management of the drainage system, that the future of the valley must be based. Once that is

Westhay Moor – before

Westhay Moor – after

assured, a return to the earlier pattern of farming should be possible, with the farmer being paid less for his less intensive form of land management. It is grossly unfair to expect the farmer alone to 'put the clock back' just for the sake of nature conservation!

The effect of agricultural 'improvements' over the past quarter of a century makes the panic engendered by the arrival of mink in 1979/80 seem in retrospect like a minor hiccup. This animal, incidentally, seems to have found its natural balance in the ecosystem, and the population of Mallard and Moorhen, most damaged when the mink arrived, are back at their previous levels. Another possible source of trouble could be the use of some drugs used to control worm infestations in cattle, and systematic insecticides used to control fly problems in piggeries. These are being closely monitored to see if they have any persistent effects on field-soil invertebrates. Fortunately here, potential problems are being foreseen and studied, so we should not end up with another persistent chemical problem.

As mentioned earlier, there are two zones of raised peat in the valley. Both have been hand-cut for centuries and this led to the superb areas they used to be, for the slow cutting out of the surface never allowed climax woodland to develop, and kept the blend of fen, carr and open pools continually reforming after the clearance of the cut-out workings. As the process extended over generations, the flora and fauna recolonised the cut-out areas as work moved on to another part of the heath. In the early 1960s, the peat industry really 'took off' and soon these fascinating heaths, the home of birds like Nightjars, Nightingales, Grasshopper Warblers and Willow Tits, became scenes of devastation: the tree- and shrub-cover was bulldozed away, the surface levelled and the mechanised block cutters and Hymac diggers moved in to remove the peat from the workings, now drying out fast due to continuous pumping. Soon the heaths were wrecked, with only small, isolated pockets of the original habitat remaining. Here, due to adjacent digging and pumping, drying out became a serious problem which persists to this day, apart from a small portion at Shapwick which has a system organised by the Nature Conservancy Council for pumping water back on to the remaining heath.

It became apparent in the 1970s that sections which had been cleared and left to part-flood and develop reed-mace and *Phragmites* beds, as well as sallows and willows, were beginning to attract birds. Where open water was allowed to stay for a year or so, Little Grebes, Moorhens, Coots and certain duck species moved in and began to breed. Unfortunately, spring pumping often ruined many breeding efforts. Reed Warblers in particular colonised reed-mace and *Phragmites* and then some places began to support Water Rails. It was soon obvious that something had to be done to try and rescue parts of the heaths from the appalling state they were in. It was no good hoping that the peat companies would just go away and leave the old

Shapwick Heath

workings to flood and revert to earlier times. Large holes in the ground have many uses: one is the dumping of waste, and some sites have been 'reclaimed' by this method already. It has been shown that the bases of the old workings can be levelled, rotavated with spoil and top soil and reseeded to grow yet more grass. Of course these sites have to be pumped out all year round and there is a rapid invasion of wetland plants making the maintenance of such pasture very expensive. Workings filled with water can be used for water sports, fishing or fish farming, or water supply. So the nature conservation organisations had to do something or they would lose out yet again. These spent workings, however they are managed, will not replace all the wildlife that was there thirty years ago, except on the small portions of part-cut peat that have been bought at great cost alongside the main purchases. Some may argue that it is wasteful to spend tens of thousands of pounds on these holes, but the potential is enormous, not only for birds but also for plants, insects, amphibians and mammals. Not to try and do something positive would be negligent, to say the least.

The STNC already owned more than 12ha of old heath on Westhay Moor and in 1986 purchased over 24ha of cleared and part-cleared workings to the north of the earlier site. One block of 4ha was already brimful of water and could not be pumped out for fear of slumping of the adjacent field. The remainder was pumped out and fully contoured before letting the water back in again. This area has some open water but, more importantly, contains a variety of habitats including islands (both bare for waders and duck loafing, and vegetated for nesting and roosting), reed-beds in shallow and deep water, carr, open wet heath and a bare peat cliff, hopefully for Kingfisher and Sand Martin nesting. This is an exciting project and could expand as adjacent workings are cleared out and enough money is found to purchase them. This area may come to resemble the ancient Somerset scene of a thousand years ago when the moors were mainly marshlands. Certainly the birds that will visit or colonise such a reserve will mostly not be those displaced by the peat-extraction industry, but the reserve should provide some sort of recompense for all the damage done to this portion of heath during the past quarter of a century. The Somerset Wildlife Appeal is in part directed to the financing of this project.

In the peat-extraction zone south of the river, the NCC already has reserves at Shapwick Heath and Canada Farm and it is planned that other parts of this area will be managed for nature conservation. The Avalon Lakes are to provide further water supplies by the end of the century. The Wessex Water Authority plan a scheme of about 400ha which will include several individual lakes, some of which will probably be for recreational use such as fishing, and some for nature conservation. This project will adjoin two areas of reserves owned by the STNC on Catcott Heath and Westhay Heath, as well as those managed by the NCC. The Somerset Peatlands Reclamation Advisory Board has been formed to facilitate and co-ordinate the future of spent workings. At Ham Wall, at the eastern end of the zone, an area of about 70ha is designated by the WWA to be used as a summer flood-relief scheme, to take any flood water from the Brue, thus preventing floods further down the valley. The water will be discharged back into the river as soon as the level falls. The whole of the Ham Wall scheme will be a joint WWA/RSPB/ NCC venture, with the probability of only about one summer flood in ten years, and the reserve management will be undertaken by the RSPB. The possibility exists of further reserves in this zone, too. The actual time of completion of all these schemes is very difficult to predict at the time of writing.

All this must reinforce the view that it is essential for the nature conservation organisations to acquire as much as possible of these vital parts of the moors and heaths to try and ensure a continued existence for all the varied wildlife of the valley.

Thanks to B. Carter, S. Davies, C.G. Hancock, B. Johnson, G. Mac-

Westhay Heath Reserve

Arthur, C. Smith, J. Stephen, B. Storer, and B. Tinkler for advice and for patiently answering numerous queries during the preparation of this section.

John McGeoch

Westward of here, the levels immediately behind the coast in the triangle Wedmore/Brean/Puriton have long been improved grassland. The brick and tile industry which flourished here and around Bridgwater in the last century has left behind a number of flooded pits which are worthy of some attention, though much disturbed. The smaller 'burrow' pits used to dig out bridge foundations along the railway line are too small to be of much interest. Across the whole area cuts the M5, finished in 1972. Like all motorways it is haunted by Kestrels and by scavenging corvids along its hard shoulder; its drivers have killed many Barn Owls in recent years. Another conspicuous feature is the Huntspill River, a cut dug to help supply water to the Ordnance Factory at Puriton in 1940, which also helped to drain the area; it is not of any great ornithological importance, except for some feeding waders and as a flight line for gulls and ducks, and a wildfowl refuge in hard weather.

THE POLDEN HILLS AND KING'S SEDGE MOOR

The narrow ridge of the Poldens runs from Somerton to Dunball, separating the peat-moors of the Brue Basin from King's Sedge Moor. Near the eastern end the top is in places no wider than the road it carries, affording spectacular views both ways. To the south-east the ridge broadens out, the plateau and its western slopes being clothed with extensive woodland, some of it managed as nature reserves: Butleigh Wood, Great Breach Wood and Copley Wood. Among other species, these hold Nightingale, Tree Pipit and Wood Warbler, besides many tits and woodpeckers. There were formerly Woodlarks.

To the south, the great waste of King's Sedge Moor began to be effectively drained from 1794, when the bold step was taken of cutting a straight outfall to replace the former wandering course of the River Cary. Despite continuing pressure in recent years, the upper end of the Moor, east of Greylake and the Taunton to Glastonbury road, remains important for its breeding waders (Lapwing, Snipe, Redshank and Curlew), as well as for Mute Swan at all seasons. The population of Yellow Wagtail and Whinchat (35 pairs in 1983) are among the highest in south-west England. It is one of the areas used by passage Whimbrel in spring. There are the remains of a number of old duck decoys, some still used as flighting ponds. The rank herbage sometimes attracts Quail. Conservation measures for these moors are imperative.

THE SOUTH-EAST

A substantial area of south-east Somerset defies ready description or a close analysis of its birds. This is a region approximately within a line joining Wells, Shepton Mallet, Bruton, Wincanton, Milborne Port, Yeovil, Langport, Somerton and Glastonbury. It is mainly a land of smallish fields, orchards and many old villages. In recent years, it has lost many hedges with their timber, and here, as elsewhere in the county, older orchards have been grubbed up and their regimented replacements are not as attractive to birds. There are many small woods, especially along the broken hills between Castle Cary and the Dorset border. Cogley Wood, near Bruton, has recently lost much of its interest, having been taken over by commercial forestry. The rivers are the upper reaches of the Brue, its northern tributary the Alham, the

Cary and the Yeo, but the streams of the extreme south-east, of which the largest is the Cale, drain into the Dorset Stour. Apart from a small lake at Compton Castle, there are no waters larger than ponds. As a whole, the area has not attracted much attention from birdwatchers, but there is probably little to be discovered apart from a good population of woodpeckers and the commoner passerines. Buzzards and Sparrowhawks are found throughout. Yellowhammers have recently increased on the hillsides around Doulting, as have Lesser Whitethroats in the upper Brue Valley. Lower down, between Bruton and Lydford, is a major winter feeding area for gulls; these are mainly Black-headed, but there is a regular flock of Common Gulls, and small parties of Lesser Black-backs occur, besides Lapwing, and some Golden Plover in hard weather. There are Grey Wagtails and Kingfishers on the Alham and the Brue, and Dippers, too, are probably regular on the latter. Both Partridges and Corn Buntings breed in the downland country of Corton Ridge, and a few Cirl Buntings remain in the Langport area. The heronry at Somerton Erleigh was once the largest in Somerset, but has been much reduced by felling of trees.

In the south-west of the area is the shapeless modern sprawl of Yeovil. Its attendant reservoir at Sutton Bingham has been carefully studied and deserves a special entry.

SUTTON BINGHAM RESERVOIR

The reservoir is about 5km south of Yeovil. Completed in 1953, it was formed by the damming of a tributary of the River Yeo. It occupies 57.5ha in a T-shape, the upright pointing south, with the extreme southern tip in Dorset, though the whole reservoir is treated as a Somerset site. The reservoir is mostly rather shallow, generally less than 10m deep, but up to 12m at the north end. It is easy to view: a road crosses the north-west end (thus creating the West Pool), this causeway providing views over most of the north end. The road continues south, parallel with and close to the reservoir, which can be observed from several gates and lay-bys all the way along. A picnic and viewing area overlooking the north end is open from March until September.

The reservoir is set in undulating mixed farmland. It is bordered by Wessex Water Authority land, mostly 'improved', often herb-rich, pasture used for grazing sheep. There is a narrow, intermittent fringe of marsh plants such as Meadowsweet and rushes, but no extensive marshy vegetation. At the southern tip of the reservoir, a dense willow copse has grown, expanding northwards and now occupying about 1ha. Hedgerows and their trees are plentiful around the reservoir, and there is some scrub and two small inaccessible woods. However, hedge removal has been noted recently, as land is converted to arable. Some aquatic plants grow around the willows and on the West Pool, but less than formerly.

The reservoir is used for trout fishing from late March to mid-October, and was once very productive. However, coarse fish have been increasing dramatically during the 1980s and appear to have taken over from the trout, which are now scarce. From the ornithological viewpoint, a second and more important consequence of the coarse fish invasion has become apparent; the abundant fish, mainly Roach and Carp, have been responsible for a severe depletion in aquatic invertebrates and plants, the food of many waterfowl. As a result, many species of waterfowl have shown sudden declines, though fish-eating species are increasing.

After much controversy, sailing was introduced in the 1960s, although restricted to the north end. West Pool is used for model boating on Sundays.

This was once the ninth most important reservoir for wildfowl in England; dabbling, grazing and diving species have all occurred in good numbers. The southern half of the reservoir and West Pool are favoured by most duck species; many duck, particularly surface-feeders, spend the daytime in the willows.

For the commonest species the table below shows: (a) the maximum recorded, (b) the highest mean maximum over five winters, and (c) the mean maximum for the three most recent winters (1984/85–1986/87):

	(a)	(b)	(c)
Wigeon	3700	1734 (1968/69–1972/73)	1350
Gadwall	45	34 (1980/81–1984/85)	12
Teal	2026	459 (1978/79–1982/83)	234
Mallard	690	396 (1980/81–1984/85)	360
Pintail	150	116 (1968/69–1972/73)	26
Shoveler	1000	308 (1969/70–1973/74)	21
Pochard	584	254 (1974/75–1978/79)	109
Tufted Duck	340	216 (1975/76–1979/80)	78

The decline in duck numbers is thought to be due to two factors. Firstly, a long-term gradual decline of some surface-feeders, due to the drainage of the South Levels, which previously attracted many wildfowl, some of which commuted to the reservoir, as they still do but in much smaller numbers. Secondly, a sudden decline in most species attributed to the population explosion of coarse fish and subsequent reduction of available food, as detailed earlier. Coot have also declined seriously, as have Bewick's Swans, which used to fly in to roost from their feeding grounds on the South Levels. An early-autumn flock of moulting Mute Swans no longer occurs, and the number of Little Grebes appear to be declining. On the positive side, the burgeoning fish population has attracted increasing numbers of Cormorants, Great Crested Grebes and Grey Herons. As in many areas, Canada Geese are increasing. Many scarce wildfowl have turned up, ranging from Smew and Ruddy Duck (almost regular in severe cold weather), to several North American species.

Breeding waterfowl are not very numerous, perhaps because of the scarcity of emergent and fringe vegetation. Mallard breed in moderate numbers, as Coot did until recently. Most significant of the remaining species are up to six pairs of Great Crested Grebes and, usually, one pair of Tufted Duck.

Waders occur mainly in autumn, particularly when the water level is low, with the shallow south end and its favoured muddy margins being most productive. Common and Green Sandpipers often pass through in good numbers, with a scattering of other species, perhaps less commonly than before. A number of rare waders from Eurasia and North America have turned up at this time. Spring passage is usually very poor, except for Common Sandpipers, partly because water levels are high at this season.

Tern passage, mainly in autumn, is rather erratic; Common and Black are the most regular species. Terns rarely stay for more than a day, and many pass almost straight through. Occurrences are often associated with rough weather or, particularly with Black Terns, south-east winds.

In recent years much effort has been put into gull-watching. Gulls are most abundant between November and March, using the reservoir for bathing and resting en route to and from coastal roosts, mainly in Dorset. The intensive observations have yielded many Mediterranean Gulls and all of Somerset's Ring-billed Gulls (but see Appendix).

A variety of other common species breed around the reservoir, including Buzzard, Lesser Whitethroat and Reed Bunting. Summer concentrations of Swifts and hirundines sometimes attract the odd Hobby. Similarly, in winter, the abundance of prey proves a draw to Peregrines. At this season, Redwings and Fieldfares often feed in moderate numbers in the surrounding pasture. Autumn, and to a lesser extent spring, sees a few migrant passerines, early mornings being best for them. Species such as pipits and wagtails often follow the axis of the reservoir south. In recent years, Ospreys have become almost annual on passage, mainly in autumn.

Coverage was apparantly poor in the early years, then more regular in the late 1960s and 1970s. The 1980s have seen an increase in coverage, which has been almost daily in some years, and over 200 species have now been observed.

Dave Chown

THE SOUTH BORDER

The southern border of the county from Yeovil to Chard forms the watershed between the Parrett, draining north to the Bristol Channel, and the Axe, flowing south-west into Devon. The varied countryside, with many small parks, mixed farming and Hamstone villages has been studied more intensively than many other rather similar areas of Somerset. This is exemplified by Tony Parson's survey of the birds of the Crewkerne area.

THE CREWKERNE DISTRICT

The Crewkerne district is primarily an area of fairly intensive agriculture, but is enhanced ornithologically by habitats associated with afforestation and game-rearing, a country park, two rivers and a large number of ponds.

In a mainly dairying area, the intensification which occurred on many farms during the 1960s and 1970s, and subsequent change in pasture management, such as increased ploughing and reseeding and silage-making, have undoubtedly had a profound effect on many birds. A prime case is that of the Curlew, which bred in five parishes in the district in the 1960s, but has not bred since 1979. In the 1980s, it would seem that the Lapwing may follow suit, although it is difficult to attribute this to one specific factor. The absence in recent years of wintering Golden Plover, which used to be annual, may also be due to changes in the pasture.

A secondary effect has been on the water quality in streams and rivers, where pollution has increased. The major sources of this are silage effluent, slurry, milk products and nitrogenous fertilisers, all of which damage sensitive invertebrate populations, and has in turn affected birds such as the Dipper, Grey Wagtail and the Kingfisher. All three species could be found throughout the Crewkerne district up to the 1960s (even if at a low density). In the late 1980s, however, they have declined to the point where breeding Dippers are now a rarity, breeding Kingfishers are uncommon and Grey Wagtails are no longer a familiar sight on what were once suitable watercourses. The River Axe, in particular, has suffered badly over a number of years and these species now rarely breed on its course. The River Parrett is less affected, but, even there, pollution is evident at times.

A further effect resulted from the trend in the late 1970s, towards

Dairy farming

maximising field-use and efficiency, by the removal of many hedgerows and patches of scrub. At the present time, this is happening less frequently.

During the 1960s and 1970s, habitat associated with the early stages of afforestation was particularly valuable to some species, such as the Tree Pipit and Grasshopper Warbler. Privatisation of much of the Forestry Commission land, including the New Plantation and Pen Wood, does not seem to have had any direct effect as yet, other than restricting access to such areas. Time has had a greater effect in that a number of plantings from the same period are now at a less useful stage to bird populations. Areas at Cricket St Thomas, Chillington, Dinnington, Hinton St George, Hardington Mandeville and Pendomer fall into this category. The Tree Pipit no longer breeds in the district, and the Grasshopper Warbler is now a rare and irregular breeder, although it is difficult to know how much of the decline is due to factors beyond the breeding area.

The list of declining or vanished populations continues with species such as the Cirl Bunting, which no longer breeds in the district. The factors affecting the Cirl Bunting are still the subject of speculation (although they are possibly climatic), but in other cases, such as the Barn Owl, a number of factors can be blamed, including the reduction of breeding sites caused by the removal or development of old barns and derelict buildings. In most years now, only one or two pairs of Barn Owls are likely to breed in the area.

Prior to the drastic national decline of the Sand Martin, small numbers could be found breeding in the road-cuttings and banks, in the wide belt of Yeovil Sand which crosses the district. The species has not bred for many years now and is only rarely seen on migration.

The Collared Dove population increased at a high rate during the 1970s. In the last few years, numbers have stabilised, and may even have declined in some parts. Two reasons put forward are the reduction in the availability of grain at mills and farms, and the associated control of the birds at these sites, involving the killing of up to 100 birds in a month at Lopen.

Development of land for commercial use or housing often affects marginal agricultural land, or that which has lain fallow for a period. This is of course particularly noticeable close to towns. The development of the Ashlands Estate at Crewkerne has removed the last two pairs of Turtle Doves from the parish and will effectively remove 20% of warbler territories.

One major change in the last twenty years has been the advent of Dutch elm disease, the death of all mature elm trees and the subsequent removal of the majority. The exact effects of this are difficult to ascertain but apparent declines in species such as the Stock Dove and Little Owl may be related, at least in part, to this. On the other hand, supposition that a major effect on the Rook population would result has not been upheld; where the Rooks were not already nesting in other trees (particularly beech, oak and ash), they have been quite ready to make the change. In fact, after a marked decrease up to the late 1970s (coincident with decreases in other species associated with seed-dressings), the Rook population now appears to be recovering; a survey of rookeries in 1985 indicated increases over 1975 and 1980. Magpies and Carrion Crows, which were not affected by grain-dressings, have markedly increased in the last twenty years, mainly due to a reduction in control of their numbers.

Other species have also increased. The Buzzard has recovered remarkably from the effects of myxomatosis on its main prey, the rabbit, and from persecution by gamekeepers; the population, at around one pair per 3sq.km, is perhaps the highest in the county. The Sparrowhawk, similarly, has recovered to the extent that it now outnumbers the Kestrel, which appears to have declined slightly. Hobbies now breed on occasion, although it is perhaps more likely that this is a reflection of increased awareness by observers rather than of an actual increase in the number of Hobbies.

The Crewkerne area is fortunate to have a good number of mature beeches, which supply winter food for some birds and nest sites for others. Most of these date from around the same time, however, and not having been followed up by later plantings, are all becoming senile over a relatively short period. Their number is decreasing annually, which could affect the lifestyles, if not the populations, of several species, including wintering Chaffinches and Bramblings, and breeding Stock Doves and Nuthatches.

The district has always held a considerable number of orchards. In recent years, these have probably increased slightly, but the trees are mostly of the small modern varieties and the value of the orchards to birds is greatly reduced in terms of nest sites and windfalls. Few breeding birds occur in the modern orchards and winter flocks of Redwings and Fieldfares are no longer attracted to and sustained by rotting apples on the ground. Bullfinches have increased, although whether this is related to the increase in the number of 'fruit farms' is not clear.

Efficiency in several areas has affected various birds' feeding habits. Modern stockyards with efficient forage stores have reduced the flocks of Yellowhammers and finches which were previously characteristic of many farms. Modern slurry lagoons are less hospitable to insects than the old dung heaps, and flocks of Meadow Pipits are now scarcer in winter around farm buildings. The reduction in the amount of fat-hen in kale and other forage crops has drastically reduced the flocks of Linnets and other finches, buntings and sparrows which fed in such crops. Indeed, the Tree Sparrow, which used to occur in small flocks, and bred in small numbers, is now a rare bird.

The closure of Crewkerne rubbish tip and the continuous sculpting of the Odcombe tip have removed most of the gulls which were characteristic of these sites in the 1960s and the 1970s.

There are now over fifty ponds in the Crewkerne district, primarily on farmland, about half of which have been developed during the last twenty years. These have resulted in increased records of breeding for Little Grebe, Canada Goose, Tufted Duck and Mallard.

The mention of water birds must, inevitably, bring a mention of mink. Their general increase and spread along the Axe and the Parrett during the last twenty years appears to have had an adverse affect on some species. The Moorhen has probably suffered most, and appears to have declined in recent years, to the extent that it no longer occurs in all suitable habitat. That this is due to predation rather than solely to the effects of pollution is endorsed by the decline relating to ponds as well as the rivers.

Within the district, increased pressure from visitors is marked only at Cricket St Thomas (a wildlife park developed in the 1960s), and at Ham Hill (now a designated Country Park). At neither site is the effect on birds severe and, without the visitors, neither would be likely to remain as valuable to wildlife for very long.

The imposition of milk quotas in the 1980s is already changing the face of agriculture, and it remains to be seen how much effect these and other quotas and restrictions will have on the wildlife of the district. It seems inevitable, however, that benefits will accrue from less intensive farming activities and associated reductions in pollution and contamination.

The change of attitude to wildlife amongst many agriculturists is exemplified by the development in the 1980s of Towntree Nature Reserve at Martock, a commercial enterprise with a system of ponds and water-meadows in what was previously farmland.

Tony Parsons

THE COAST FROM BREAN DOWN TO HINKLEY POINT

Brean Down, a limestone headland that extends about 1.5km into the Bristol Channel, lies at the most northerly point of the Somerset coast. With its highest point at about 97m, it rises well above the surrounding land. At the eastern end is the mouth of the River Axe, which forms the border with Avon. The estuary is much disturbed by boating activity at high tide, and rarely holds more than a small number of duck and waders, but several hundred gulls feed at the sewage outflow on the ebbing tide.

The Down is well covered with bracken and brambles; there are also plenty of bushes, mainly hawthorn, elder and privet, and there are a few larger trees near the farm at the south-east corner. Attempts have been made to control the spread of the bracken and brambles, not only by cutting, but also by the introduction of goats and cattle, and it will be interesting to see what effect this has on the ground-nesting birds and those, like the Willow Warbler, who need low cover in which to nest. If grassy areas are kept too short by grazing, then species such as Skylark and Meadow Pipit, which have suffered by the original encroachment of bracken, will be under further pressure. Nesting birds may face the added disturbance as newly-opened areas, previously difficult to reach, become more accessible to holiday-makers and walkers.

Such worries pale, however, against the devastation likely to be caused by the proposed Severn Barrage from here to Lavernock Point in Wales. The environmental effects of this seem to be poorly understood by planners, and it is possible that not only birds but several varieties of rare plants and insects face destruction. It would totally alter the character of the Channel and its ecosystem, the accumulation of silt and waste products would undoubtedly

Brean Down

be a problem, and the net result will be the loss of feeding grounds for many wintering and passage waders. The Severn Estuary holds 12 per cent of all Dunlin wintering in Britain, and with its specialized feeding habits, males and females requiring different kinds of mudflat, this species is especially threatened (Clark, 1987). Conservationists must continue to hope that this ambitious engineering project, still by no means certain to proceed, fails at the planning stage, and that Brean Down remains largely unchanged, and still the most likely site in the county to find rare passerine migrants.

An interesting feature of the whole coast, and one often witnessed here, is the visible migration of hundreds, or even thousands, of Chaffinches, Starlings, Greenfinches and Linnets. In most years, scarcer species, sometimes even Woodlarks and Crossbills, move with the flocks.

An extensive area of sand dunes stretches southwards from the Down, separating the sea from low-lying farmland to the east; this is an area of well-ditched alluvial clay grassland, with many hedges and a few trees. Beyond the dunes, at low tide, vast areas of soft mud are exposed.

The dunes, where Woodlark and Stonechat once bred, are now largely built over, and holiday development continues apace, with the growth of

Berrow – dunes and reed-beds

leisure centres and camping sites. Erosion of the dunes, despite attempts to funnel holiday-makers down well-marked paths, may well become a serious problem. Sandy areas still undeveloped are invaded by Sea Buckthorn, an aggressive plant introduced about 1890 to stabilise the dunes. Its expansion into grassy areas has affected species such as Skylark and Meadow Pipit and even the Linnet for, although the buckthorn provides abundant nesting sites for this little finch, its food plants are squeezed out.

At Berrow, a salt-marsh has been created behind the dune system. This area has been extensively studied and is of considerable ornithological value (Slade, 1981). A diverse vegetation includes the Mediterranean Rush, at its only known British site, and the diversity is reflected in the large number of species that have been recorded here over the years. Regular breeding birds have included Grasshopper Warblers as well as the more common Reed and Sedge, and Bearded Tits often feed among the *Phragmites*.

The surrounding golf course probably provides a degree of immunity from more damaging forms of development, but some threat still exists. In 1973, the construction of a new nine-hole course destroyed some of the main marsh and the associated marginal vegetation and breeding habitat for Stonechats; the creation of two small ponds, of little ornithological value, was scant consolation. Nevertheless, the area has repaid regular watching: breeding

Berrow – salt marsh

Hoopoes fed here in 1977, and recent rarities have included Yellow-breasted Bunting, Short-toed Lark and Serin.

Natural progression is converting the original marsh to scrub and creating a new one within the dune system. Already, one or two pairs of Reed and Sedge Warblers are established in the new salt-marsh and, in winter, the occasional Snow and Lapland Bunting and Shore Lark may be flushed from the shore.

To the south, at the mouth of the River Brue, lies Burnham-on-Sea. Once a genteel seaside resort, it is rapidly losing this identity as, with the construction of the M5 motorway, it has increasingly become a dormitory town for Bristol and beyond, with consequent suburban expansion. Lanes where Cirl Buntings once sang are now submerged by large housing developments, but not all the news is depressing. Attempts to develop the parks and brick-pits, which may be quite productive for birds, have met with encouragingly fierce resistance from local residents. The Burnham sea front is a bizarre mixture of the Victorian and the hideously garish, which does little credit to local planners. Although the area was neglected for sea-watching in the past, recent study has proved many species of seabird to be far less rare than previously supposed. Westerly gales, particularly during high tides in September and October, blow in Storm and Leach's Petrels, shearwaters, Sabine's Gulls, Kittiwakes and skuas with some regularity.

Burnham-on-Sea is on the eastern boundary of Bridgwater Bay, into which drain the Rivers Brue, Parrett and Huntspill. Much of this comprises the National Nature Reserve of the NCC, which has built a number of hides of debatable value on the west side of the Parrett at Steart. The whole area is in urgent need of a long-term management plan, not only to fully realise the ornithological potential of the Steart site, but to improve the sterile area of farmland bordering the Huntspill River; heavily grazed by sheep, this is now of diminishing ornithological interest.

Steart Island, which once held an important gull colony and is still a site for Ringed Plovers, faces pressure from human activity; boats now land with impunity in all seasons despite restrictions, water-skiers traverse the nearby channels, and the area is regularly shot over in winter, to the detriment of

Parrett Estuary

wildfowl and waders. Despite all this, the bay is of immense value to a wide variety of species: it is an important moulting ground for Shelduck; in winter and on migration, thousands of Dunlin, with smaller numbers of Oyster-catcher, Grey Plover, Curlew, and Redshank, frequent the mudflats. Less common, but not infrequent, are Little Stint and Curlew Sandpiper, with the occasional Avocet, and in most autumns vagrant transatlantic waders occur. Two species, both of which have declined, deserve special mention: Black-tailed Godwit used to number over 1000 in autumn, but now barely reach 200; Whimbrel, which use the area as a staging post on northward migration, have decreased from as many as 2000 to only a few hundred; the reasons for this are unknown. Birds of prey that regularly hunt the area in winter include Hen Harrier, Peregrine and Merlin and the ubiquitous Kestrel. Marsh Harrier and Red Kite have been seen on passage.

In 1929, Cord Grass (*Spartina*) was introduced to the mudflats opposite Wall Common by the then Somerset River Board, in the hope that it would build up the level of the foreshore and reduce wave attack on the shingle and earth banks which formed the only means of coastal protection along that part of the coast. It subsequently spread to cover some 100ha by 1968, extending in a band about 3.2km long and about 400m wide. The foreshore has been built up by as much as 2m, but it is thought unlikely that these colonized mudflats will ever progress into a fully developed salting because of the very turbulent tidal conditions which undermine the root systems, thereby causing erosion (Morley, 1973).

This introduction of an alien plant reduced the feeding area for waders, but it was probably not significant when related to several thousand hectares of mudflats still remaining in the bay. *Spartina* beds appear to be a rather sterile habitat as far as birds are concerned: few species feed on the seeds, and it is probably only of use as a roost for a few ducks, waders, Water Rails and the odd Short-eared Owl. It may prove, as it has in some parts of the country, to be a menace and very difficult to eradicate.

As the upper shores increase in height, new species of plants colonize the area, especially Glasswort *Salicornia spp.*, Orache *Atriplex spp.*, Sea Beet *Beta vulgaris*, Sea Blite *Suaeda maritima*, and Sea Aster *Aster tripolium*. It is these plants that provide good winter feeding for the flocks of finches and buntings.

It was in about 1952 that the Common Reed *Phragmites australis* began to colonise the upper shore, along with the Reed-mace *Typha latifolia*, and these have since rapidly extended to cover most of the upper shore between Wall Common and Fenning. In these extensive reed-beds, Aquatic Warblers have been proved almost annual, and many other rare passerine migrants doubtless remain undiscovered in the surrounding area due to lack of coverage.

For a detailed study of the birds of the Bridgwater Bay Reserve, see Morley (1986).

To the west of Steart lies the area of Wall Common. Behind the shingle bank is an easily-walked coastal path to Stolford and beyond to Hinkley Point; interesting species here have included wintering Shore Larks, as well as Snow and Lapland Buntings.

Hinkley Point itself is dominated by the nuclear power station complex; a small Herring Gull colony exists here. On the seaward side, the warm-water discharge has until recently received little attention from bird-watchers; this may well change, however, now that Little Gulls have been found to be regular in winter, and with the recent sightings of an Iceland Gull and a Forster's Tern. As we write, pressure groups are girding their loins in an attempt to thwart the building of a third reactor at the site. The ornithological effects of this will certainly be detrimental to some species on site, such as the small and vulnerable population of Nightingales. It is ironic that in preference to nuclear power, the proposed 'alternative' form of power, the Severn Barrage, provokes as much, if not more, outcry. For a detailed study on the area, see Robins (1985).

The whole of the coast faces development pressures all too familiar in other parts of the country, and much of the action of organised conservation bodies is inevitably rearguard. However, not all of the avian changes have been depressing. On the credit side, a small population of Bearded Tits is now established at one site, Water Rails probably breed more frequently than records suggest, and Cetti's Warblers have taken up residence at one or two sites. Most changes, however, are undoubtedly for the worse, and it is hoped that future authors on this important length of coastline will be able to report with greater optimism.

Brian Hill and Brian Slade

BRIDGWATER AND THE EASTERN SLOPES OF THE QUANTOCKS

The town has always been important as a strategic and commercial centre. The docks are now closed. As elsewhere, Herring Gulls have tried to colonise the roofs, but have met with strong resistance. The brick industry has gone, but industrial development led in 1936 to the construction of Durleigh Reservoir to the west of the town. Here, from 1948, the statistical basis of

Durleigh Reservoir

National Wildfowl Counts was established by a series of counts made by
Eileen Palmer and analysed by G.V.T. Mathews (Atkinson-Willes, 1963).
The reservoir is much disturbed by fishing, yet remains of interest not only
for its relatively small duck population but also for its use as a roost by the
herd of Bewick's Swans that feed on the levels to the south-east. It attracts
migrants from the nearby coast at Steart. Further west are Ashford
Reservoir, which is very small but has one of the few current Sand Martin
colonies in Somerset, and Hawkridge Reservoir, with some winter ducks,
and surrounding woodland which is good for birds of prey.

The brick industry left Bridgwater with a ring of small flooded pits, some

Screech Owl Ponds, Huntworth

of which have small reed-beds and bushy cover. The most important are: Screech Owl Pits at Huntworth, now a reserve; the nearby Dunwear Pits; Chilton Trinity Pits to the north-west of the town; and, further down river, Combwich. At Huntworth is a complicated rail- and roadscape, with the elevated section of the M5 passes over one of the few remaining substantial areas of *Phragmites*. However, at Combwich, most of the reed-beds have been grubbed out and flooded, and now attract very few birds; Chilton Trinity suffers from dumping, infilling, and recreational disturbance, and lies in the path of a proposed bypass to carry traffic round the north side of the town. Bitterns have probably bred in the area, but not very recently; the newly arrived Cetti's Warblers have found the thick cover congenial. Much ringing of *Acrocephalus* warblers has been done at Combwich, although this has all but ceased now due to the loss of habitat. Further north-west, the coast is dominated by the square towers of Hinkley Point Power Station (begun in 1958); to the south-west lie the Quantocks, discussed here in more detail.

THE QUANTOCKS

The Quantock Hills range for 20km in a south-easterly direction from the coast and are of Devonian rock. They reach a height of 384m at Will's Neck. To the south-west the slopes are very steep, and the combes little more than indentations in the escarpment, with no considerable streams, but in the east they are long, winding, and well-wooded. To the north, the woodland is mostly broad-leaved (Hodder's Combe, Holford Combe, Bin Combe), but further south the large conifer plantations of the Forestry Commission are dominant (Quantock Combe, Ram's Combe, Cockercombe). Habitats include dwarf shrub heath, both wet (Heather, Cross-leaved Heath and Bilberry) and dry (Bell Heather, Gorse, Bristle Bent and Bilberry); acidic flushes by some streams (Cottongrass, Sundew and Bog-Pimpernel); and dense scrub (Sessile Oak, Downy Birch, Hawthorn and Holly). The ancient semi-natural broad-leaved woodland is of Birch and Sessile Oak. Bracken covers large areas of the higher sloping ground.

Crowcombe Park Gate, Quantocks

In summer above the tree-line one can occasionally find Hobbies chasing Swifts or insects, and in the evening one can hear the Nightjar, which, although decreasing nationally, seems to be holding its own here; a BTO survey in 1981 recorded 27 singing males. Skylarks and Meadow Pipits are common, the latter heavily predated by Cuckoos. Whinchats arrive in spring and hold territory over most of the land above the tree-line; Stonechats are resident, though their numbers, here as elsewhere, have been affected by cold winters. Wheatears occasionally breed and Ring Ouzels may be seen on spring passage. Warblers are represented on the higher ground by Grasshopper Warbler and Whitethroat; there have been several records of Dartford Warbler. Ravens used to be fairly common, but now only a few pairs breed.

In the broad-leaved woodland, Sparrowhawks are found, Buzzards are common, as are Tawny Owls, which are more often heard than seen. Nuthatches and Treecreepers are fairly common, and all three woodpeckers occur, the Lesser Spotted being the most difficult to find, as it lives mostly in the topmost branches. Grey Wagtails are resident by the streams, but Dippers have unfortunately disappeared from a number of former haunts, though a few pairs still breed. All the usual tits occur, forming mixed flocks in winter, sometimes with Goldcrests and the occasional Willow Tit. Jays are fairly common, although shy. Among summer visitors, Willow and Wood Warblers are numerous, especially the former, and there are some Garden Warblers. During the last days of April, Pied Flycatchers arrive from their African winter quarters. Though naturally nesting in holes in trees, they will readily use nestboxes, which have helped to improve the population from a maximum of three pairs, in 1948–58, to about thirty pairs today. Redstarts will also use nestboxes, but not as readily, and their numbers remain steady at about thirty pairs. Turtle Doves are not often heard now, except in one or two favoured spots. Tree Pipits tend to prefer the tops of the combes, where they have space in the more open woodland for their song-flights. In the winter months, large flocks of Chaffinches can be disturbed from their feeding among the beechmast, Woodcock can be found probing in the boggy areas, and Siskins and Redpolls visit the alders in the combe bottoms.

The conifer tracts have many breeding Goldcrests, whose numbers may be depleted after hard winters. Siskins have bred recently, with up to ten singing males at one site, and there are summer records of Redpolls too. Parties of Crossbills can occasionally be found.

Two notable birds have disappeared from the area. The Black Grouse has probably been extinct on Quantock since the end of the 1970s, though it was once common; large numbers were shot for sport. Red-backed Shrikes have vanished, as elsewhere, following the contraction of their northern breeding range.

The Quantocks are increasingly used by hikers, riders, campers and scramblers, and there are frequent heath fires. There are also pressures from quarrying interests. A large area has now been made a SSSI by the Nature Conservancy Council. There is a good wardening system, with a permanent warden and volunteer wardens, and we hope this will afford the area at least some protection.

John Chidgey

THE PARRETT BASIN

The Parrett upstream from Bridgwater is a canalised muddy ditch winding between long-reclaimed farmland. Underneath the Mump at Burrow Bridge it is joined by the Tone from the south-west, and to the east of this confluence the area of Southlake Moor (now an SSSI) is subject to controlled flooding to take overspill in times of pressure. This system now seems likely to continue, to the benefit of swans and some duck and Coot. The drainage systems of the Parrett and the Cale are linked here, with Aller Moor and North Moor leading north to King's Sedge Moor. Further up the Parrett, West Sedge Moor opens to the south-west. This critical area is partly a reserve of the RSPB.

North Moor/Aller Moor

WEST SEDGE MOOR

West Sedge Moor lies between the North Curry to Stoke St Gregory ridge and the Fivehead to Curry Rivel ridge. The River Parrett, which is elevated and embanked at this point, cuts across the north-east end of the Moor on its way to the sea. The West Sedge Moor pumping station evacuates excess water from the moor into the Parrett, whilst in the summer months water is let on to the moor from the river to maintain levels at the required height. The moor consists of just over 1000ha of meadows, each of which is bounded by water ditches, and is virtually level. The soil is mostly peat and the water table varies between ground level in winter to about 45cm below it in summer. During most winters one or two small floods occur, which are pumped off in about five days. Occasionally a larger flood may persist for up to a fortnight.

The great majority of the meadows are pastures, though a few are used to grow potatoes or arable crops. There are also a few withy-beds which supply the local basket-making industry. A large proportion of the meadows are of

West Sedge Moor

high botanical interest, with a good variety of wetland plants. They can look impressively beautiful in the summer months. From July, the majority are cut for hay, and are then grazed until conditions become too wet, usually around November.

These damp, peaty meadows with the late hay-cut are good for breeding Lapwing, Snipe, Curlew and Redshank, though their numbers have declined markedly in recent years. The ditch systems, too, are good for wildlife, and support a variety of plants, insects, mammals and birds.

Drainage operations over several centuries have converted West Sedge Moor from a marsh to farmland. However, the process is not complete; the land is not fully dried out and farming operations are limited. It is technically possible to improve drainage further, but it is very expensive and not justified in the present agricultural climate. Back in the 1960s and 1970s, however, the possibility of further drainage and loss of wildlife was very real and the wildlife conservation bodies were concerned. The best areas on the levels have now been notified as SSSIs by the Nature Conservancy Council, which has also purchased land in a number of places. The Somerset Trust for Nature Conservation has also been actively buying land on various parts of the levels, and much of the area is now one of the Government's 'Environmentally Sensitive Areas', so the value of the Somerset Levels for landscape and wildlife is now established. Somerset County Council has been active in reconciling the differences of the various parties involved.

The RSPB began to buy land on West Sedge Moor in 1978, with more purchases in succeeding years. The original ownerships were very fragmented, with many different owners owning small parcels of land – some owning only one field. In spite of this, the RSPB now owns about 365ha on the moor, some of it in reasonably large blocks. It soon became apparent that the nearby strip of woodland along the south-east side of the moor contained a rich and diverse wildlife, as well as being a prominent and much valued feature of the landscape. It holds some fine carpets of the commoner woodland plants such as Bluebells, Primroses and Anemones, as well as more unusual species in the form of various orchids, Herb Paris and False Oxslips. Birdlife includes Buzzards, Sparrowhawks and Kestrels, a large heronry and a good variety of the smaller woodland species, including Nightingales. Foxes, Badgers and Roe Deer are common. Like the moor, the woodland has many owners, but eight blocks totalling about 40ha have been bought and form part of the RSPB reserve.

When the Society has purchased land on the moor, usually from local farmers, it has usually rented it back to them on an annual basis, provided it is farmed in a traditional manner. A few of the meadows had been abandoned by the previous owners as too difficult to farm. One has been left in a very rough state, as it forms a winter roost for Short-eared Owls and sometimes

Hen Harriers. It also has a thriving breeding population of Sedge Warblers, Whinchats and Reed Buntings. This field and five others are used in an experimental high-water-level management scheme. Other meadows which have a high botanical interest are farmed without artificial fertilisers, whilst other agriculturally improved meadows are farmed with moderate amounts of artificials.

Much time has been spent monitoring and recording the wildlife, both on the bought land and on the rest which remains in private ownership. Some experimental work has been done, mainly looking at ways and means of raising water levels in winter and spring, and a certain amount of time and effort has been devoted to arrangements for visitors.

Since the reserve was established in 1978 there have been some changes in the moor. Agricultural improvements in some places have resulted in the loss of some meadows rich in flowers. This occurred after private drainage schemes were installed. Balancing this has been the return to a high water system of some drained fields bought by the RSPB. A number of these are once again very rich botanically. The botanical interest has, however, generally improved considerably since 1978.

Another change for the better concerns wintering ducks. In the early years of the reserve it was apparent that very few ducks spent the winter here. True, there could be up to 12,000 Wigeon, Teal and Mallard in flood conditions, but they were normally only present for a few days. When the floods went the ducks followed suit. In recent years ducks have increased on the comparatively small areas where we have raised water levels. It appears that full ditches with a little overspill onto low-lying land can be attractive to them, and during the winter of 1986/87 about 1500 were present: about 900 Teal, with 300 each of Mallard and Wigeon, plus small numbers of Pintail and Shoveler.

A serious cause for concern, however, is the decline in numbers of breeding waders, not only on West Sedge Moor but over the levels as a whole. The reason is thought to be the lowering of the water levels by the drainage authorities in the late 1970s. Certainly the meadows are drier in the critical months of May and June than they were a few years ago. In the few areas where water levels have been kept up, usually on nature reserves, the waders still persist, but elsewhere they are either drastically reduced or absent altogether. Getting them back presents a challenge for the future.

A rather low population of Moorhens and low productivity from breeding Mallard has been put down to predation by mink, but suddenly, in 1987, Moorhens were once again common and Mallard bred well. A pair of Little Grebes also bred successfully. Did mink have a bad year for some reason, or are the birds beginning to get the measure of them? We await the 1988 season with interest. The populations of Sedge Warblers, Reed Buntings and

Whinchats remain steady. These birds usually nest in the dense herbage along the ditch-sides, but Yellow Wagtails have declined somewhat in recent years. This could be due to a reduction in cattle-grazing in favour of hay.

Woodland is a much more stable habitat than farmland, and the numbers of woodland species therefore tend to be more stable, with only severe winter weather to cause appreciable changes. It is worth mentioning that the hedgerows between the woodland and the moorland hold very high numbers of breeding birds, particularly warblers, the Blackcap and Chiffchaff being very common. Any scrubby areas adjoining the woodland are also very good, with many breeding pairs, and they often provide good winter roosting areas.

In the immediate future the RSPB hopes to raise the water levels over a substantial area of the reserve in an attempt to increase the number of breeding waders. As mentioned earlier, May and June are critical, because the meadows can dry out quite rapidly. The problem lies in maintaining a

Black-tailed Godwit

damp soil at this time and a dry one in the succeeding months for the farming operations. It is also the intention to increase the amount of winter flooding, thus attracting more wildfowl and waders.

Management of the woodland is going to be a long-term affair. The general aim will be to maintain the outside appearance of the woods as a landscape feature whilst gradually achieving a varied age and species structure inside them. Coppicing of the undergrowth will no doubt play a large part and we hope we will have woodland that is both pleasant to be in and good for the wildlife.

The object of the RSPB reserve is to provide a disturbance-free environment for wildlife, particularly birds, while a secondary objective is to show the wildlife to the people, providing this can be done without causing any undue disturbance. The main objective could be achieved fairly easily by simply closing up the area concerned, but the second could be more difficult. At West Sedge Moor we have provided some limited visitor facilities. There is a small car park in Swell Wood with a hide about 55m away. This hide will normally provide close views of woodland birds in winter and spring. Part of

Winter flooding

the heronry is just in front of the hide and good views of the Herons can be had until the oak canopy hides them in mid-June. There is a pleasant woodland footpath close by.

On the moor, bird-watching can be difficult. It is a large open area and the birds usually see us before we see them, and either hide in the vegetation or fly off. The wintering flocks can be at the eastern end or in the middle, or on the neighbouring moors. Floods are very infrequent, but access tracks are often wet, muddy and rutted. In the circumstances the best we can do at the present is to provide a hide on the edge of the moor, giving a good overall view. This can give interesting sightings at long range, but can be very disappointing for people expecting a Slimbridge or a Minsmere.

West Sedge Moor, with the adjacent woodland, is undoubtedly a most interesting reserve, with a wide variety of birds, mammals, plants and insects. The various management schemes envisaged should make it even better in the future.

John Humphrey, Warden

If we continue up the Parrett to Langport, the South Levels open beyond us. It is interesting that Midelney Manor, near Drayton, has one of the few surviving medieval mews; what a falconry centre it must have been then.

THE SOUTH LEVELS AND THE ISLE VALLEY

The three most important moors comprising the South Levels are Wet Moor (Muchelney), King's Moor/Witcombe Bottom (Long Load), and West Moor (Hambridge). Undoubtedly, Wet Moor when flooded holds the greatest attraction and it is especially noted for large numbers of Bewick's Swans. During the 1960s it might stay flooded from November through to March and attracted vast numbers of wildfowl. Since the large new pumps at Long Load became operational in the mid-1970s, flooding has only occurred after exceptionally heavy rain and even then is dispersed within a few days. The resultant drier conditions have allowed much improvement of the grassland overall, and at Witcombe Bottom some arable crops are grown.

All this has had a drastic effect on the typical breeding species like Curlew, Redshank, Snipe, Lapwing, Yellow Wagtail and Whinchat, which have been reduced to a very few pairs.

Basket-weaving still survives and withy-beds can still be seen on West Moor, which attract increasing numbers of Reed Warblers, though Sedge

Bewick's Swans

Warblers seem to be decreasing and Marsh Warblers have not been seen for many years. Redstarts have all but disappeared from the rows of pollarded willows, and Corn Buntings are no longer present.

A taste of what could be possible occurred during May and June 1979, when prolonged heavy rain on 30 May caused the River Yeo to flood a large part of Wet Moor. Between 5 and 14 June, the flood attracted a great variety of species, including concentrations of 40 Grey Herons, 21 Mute Swans, 77 Mallard, 7 Pochard, 6300 Lapwing, 4 Black-tailed Godwits, 8 Ringed Plovers, 1 Little Stint, 4 Black Terns, 1 Common Terns, 1 Marsh Harrier and 13 Yellow Wagtails. Large numbers of gulls found easy pickings from the mass of dead fish and earthworms, including 250 Lesser Black-backed and 2200 Black-headed. Interestingly, about 30 pairs of Black-headed Gulls built nests and at least one egg was found after the water disappeared on 17 June. Other species seen displaying included 3 pairs of Great Crested Grebes, 1 pair of Little Grebes, 5 Shelduck (one prospecting a hollow willow tree), 6 pairs of Coot, 3 pairs each of Snipe and Redshank, and 1 pair of Curlew.

To the south-west of the Levels lies the Isle Valley, which is not particularly rich in birds. It has few outstanding habitat features; the River Isle flows through a mixed dairy and arable scene with a few scattered woods. However, one of the better sections between Cock's Bridge and Hort Bridge has been bisected by the Ilminster bypass, which has necessitated diverting the course of the river between concrete embankments at Cock's Bridge, and the construction of a very obtrusive flyover to carry the B3168 road.

Variable flooding sometimes occurs between Isle Brewers and Hambridge, which can attract a few dabbling ducks and Bewick's Swans. A few pairs of Dippers and Grey Wagtails can be found on the faster-flowing stretches of the river, and perhaps the odd pair of Kingfishers may still persist.

THE BLACKDOWNS

The Blackdown Hills are the north part of the range which rises fairly abruptly out of the plain to form a wall along the south edge of Taunton Deane, and which extends south across east Devon to the English Channel.

Somerset can claim only the steep north escarpment, the north-east corner and the eastern extension. Steep-sided valleys cut into the undulating plateau, which is generally between 250 and 280m, Staple Hill at 315m being the highest point. It is generally made up of small farms, mainly of dairy or livestock-rearing, with small fields and very little arable. There are many scattered hamlets linked by narrow lanes. Hedgerows are typically earth and local chert banks topped with beech, with large trees in some areas.

Oak and ash are also allowed to grow to maturity, though hedge cutting by mechanical flail is practised. The hills are capped by small fields of clay and flint and offer little attraction to birds compared to the Greensand scarps and valley sides on the northern face. The upper slopes are covered with woodland, scrub or bracken, though Sampford Point at the extreme north-west corner is an exception, being an open hillside of grass, gorse and heather which sweeps away south over the Devon border to Culmstock Beacon. Some conifer planting has slightly reduced the open area in recent years but it did attract a few Nightjars, at least for a time; this species was quite plentiful and well-scattered over these hills but has now become rare in spite of abundant suitable habitat.

The woodland and escarpments to the east are full of warblers, with Wood Warbler being the characteristic bird of mature beech and oak; it has steadily increased. Pied Flycatchers have also become more regular, with definite breeding in 1986 and 1987. Tree Pipits are widespread in the more open areas, but Redstarts and Stonechats are declining, and Woodlarks no longer occur. Lapwing and Curlew have virtually disappeared from the open or marshy areas.

Large blocks of conifers are widespread and increasing, and of the more recent plantings one to be particularly scorned is in the wet valley at Mount Fancy, below Staple Hill. However, Buzzards, Sparrowhawks, and Kestrel are regular and the occasional Hobby can be seen. Ravens are present in this area, suggesting perhaps the odd breeding pair. Deciduous trees are still plentiful on the north-facing slopes and also at Prior's Park which is on the western limits of the Nightingales' range.

Apart from the northern slopes, there are patches of woodland, bracken and scrub on the sides of the valleys but few large areas of wild country.

Springs are plentiful, especially at the base of the downwash of the Greensand, and these seldom dry out. The Rivers Culm, Otter and Yarty rise close together in Somerset in the north-east corner of the Blackdowns. Many lesser streams also rise on the slopes and flow north or north-east to join the Tone, Parrett and Isle.

There are some areas of standing water but they hold no great attraction for birds. The largest are the reservoirs at Blagdon and Leigh Hill. At Otterhead Pumping Station a series of lakes was formed by damming the River Otter not far from its source. This is a new Trust reserve and consequently it is under greater pressure from visitors than previously; but it may still attract Little Grebe, Mallard and Coot, with Dipper and Grey Wagtail on the river. A small lake in the woodland near Witch Lodge has been upgraded and used for fishing. It formerly held a pair of Mute Swans and several pairs of Coot, but these have disappeared due to increased pressure.

David E. Paull

THE VALLEY OF THE TONE

Returning to Burrow Bridge, we can turn south-west up the Tone; 'up' is a relative word, since even at the bottom end of Taunton the height above sea level is only 12m. Beyond Athelney, Curry Moor lies to the north and Hay Moor to the south. Both have some importance for wintering Mute and Bewick's Swans. Not until Taunton itself is passed does one lose all contact with the great level. The town has a roof-top colony of Herring Gulls. Both here and and further up the Tone, small colonies of Sand Martins may still occur, though at present they are at a very low ebb. From

Taunton to the Devon border at White Ball (where Sand Martins have also bred) the red-earth farms and orchards are unsensational, but Buzzards are common, and there are Kingfishers and Dippers on the main stream and some of its tributaries. The Vale of Taunton Deane has been shown to be an important flyway for gulls at passage seasons, especially Lesser Black-backed, and there have been records of terns. In addition, Shelduck have been recorded flying north during the summer months to the moulting ground at Steart.

THE BRENDON HILLS

The Brendons are divided from the Quantocks by the valleys of the Doniford Stream to the north and the Back Stream through Bishop's Lydeard to the south. The railway line, which takes the lowest route from Norton Fitzwarren to Watchet, is a convenient boundary. Along the western slopes of the Quantocks there is a succession of old parks with good timber (Bagborough, Cothelstone, Crowcombe). Further west there is still some lowland heath on the west of the railway and boggy ground nearby; Water Rails have recently bred near Stogumber. Further south-west, a large area of lowland heath at Langford Heathfield has recently become a Trust reserve.

The Brendon Hills consist of a central east–west ridge, followed by the Bishop's Lydeard to Wheddon Cross road; by common agreement, 'Exmoor' begins at the Wheddon Cross col and west of the road from there south to Exebridge. North and south of the ridge there are deep wooded valleys, but, to the south, tongues of farmland plateau stretch out between them. In the eighteenth century, the uplands probably resembled Exmoor, though they are lower, and Black Grouse persisted on several commons until recently; the name of Heathpoult Cross commemorates them. In the last century, a mining industry came and went, and almost all the higher ground was enclosed on an Exmoor-pattern of largish fields and beech hedges. The resulting landscape is almost birdless, except for corvids, feeding Common Gulls in winter, passing Buzzards, and a few hedgerow Chaffinches and Robins. Such heathland as remained on the north side, and the western outlier of Croydon Hill, have largely been afforested. Some parts are mature enough to attract breeding Siskins, and clear-felled areas provide some of the best Nightjar habitat in the county. The Buzzard population is probably higher on the Brendons than on much of Exmoor.

The steep-sided valleys to the south proved ideal for the building of the two big post-war reservoirs. The first of these, Clatworthy, is an impressive site, with Canada Geese breeding regularly, but is too deep to attract many wildfowl. The second, Wimbleball, deserves a section to itself.

WIMBLEBALL RESERVOIR

Situated at the southern edge of the Brendon Hills, Wimbleball lies just inside the Exmoor National Park. The name Wimbleball, its origin uncertain, is taken from one of the nearby woods, part of which was felled during the construction of the dam. This 162ha reservoir, more appropriately named a lake, fits naturally in the valleys with their steeply-wooded sides and more gentle agricultural slopes.

Wimbleball Reservoir

One of the main inputs of water into the lake comes from the River Haddeo, rising about 5km north of the village of Upton; its progress is now interrupted, before it continues its journey from the dam through the Hartford Wood, to its confluence with the River Exe. Numerous smaller streams enter the lake, the largest of which is the Withiel Florey stream, more frequently referred to as the Bessom, after the main road-bridge which traverses the lake and forms the boundary to the nature reserve at its northern creek.

The reserve was established in 1978 and includes 20ha of woodland, scrub, rough grassland, marsh and a developing reed-bed. The one area of woodland is a mature larch plantation with ash, rowan and holly also present. More recently some of the conifers have been replaced by plantings of oak, maple and cherry.

Around the southern flank of the lake, woodland, both deciduous and conifer, predominates. Most of this is broadleaf; some, such as Wimbleball Wood and West Hill Wood, has been identified as ancient indigenous woodland consisting of sessile oak and birch, either as coppice or high forest.

Wimbleball was designated not only to meet the increasing demands for water, but also to blend with and enhance the beauty of the surrounding countryside, and much emphasis was put on the landscaping and conservation of the area. Water-tolerant trees such as willows and alders were planted around the edges of the lake, some eventually becoming submerged at high water level. Other species including beech, birch and poplar were planted on higher ground.

The Canada Geese are now a familiar sight feeding along the grassy perimeters of the lake or on the adjacent farmland. In winter, numbers often exceed 200; a few Barnacle and Emperor Geese and other exotics consort with the flock, which regularly commutes to Clatworthy Reservoir and the coastal fields between Minehead and Dunster Beach. Occasionally passing White-fronted or Brent Geese will pause to feed, but rarely remain for very long.

The numbers of duck wintering on the lake are usually dependent on the weather conditions; severe winters will bring in larger numbers, provided the lake does not freeze over. The commoner ducks are represented by Mallard and Teal, up to about 200, with Wigeon in larger flocks at times. Smaller numbers of Tufted Duck and Pochard, with a few Goldeneye, are also regular visitors. Shelduck, Gadwall, Shoveler and Scaup are all infrequent. Goosanders begin to arrive in November; this is a favourite winter refuge for these large sawbills, who prefer the quieter, more secluded parts of the lake. The largest influx tends to be in late winter, possibly birds on migration or temporarily roosting; as many as 40 have been recorded. Hard-weather movements will bring in rarities – Smew, Ruddy Duck or Red-breasted

Merganser – and perhaps a diver may also turn up. Coot numbers steadily build up from late summer, and reach a peak in mid-winter, with up to 300 in some years.

Wimbleball does not attract large concentrations of waders. In the winter months, when the lake is full, few suitable areas exist where they can feed, therefore most occur on spring and autumn passage. Spring passage is less obvious, and is usually notable only for a few Common Sandpipers (sometimes an overwintering bird may still be present), for Whimbrels passing northwards and for the occasional Curlew, surprisingly scarce here. As the summer progresses the receding water level exposes large muddy areas where the feeder streams enter the lake; at this time the return passage of waders is more evident. From late June onwards small numbers of Common Sandpipers appear, Green Sandpipers are regular in the reserve, and Greenshank and Wood Sandpipers may also be found. Dunlin, Ringed Plovers and Redshank have been noted. Lapwing flocks are not uncommon; small flocks often congregate near the lake edge and in spring pairs display over adjacent damp fields and farmland, although no breeding has ever been confirmed. Snipe, absent throughout the summer, can be flushed from nearby marshes and bogs at other times of the year.

Only a few species of wildfowl actually nest at Wimbleball; most are migratory and have left the lake by early April. The success of those that remain is often dependent upon a constant high water level throughout the breeding season. Great Crested Grebes, usually only the one pair, have bred annually since 1985. Canada Geese have suffered mixed fortunes, as some nests have been swamped owing to their close proximity to the water. The introduction of artificial floating islands in the nature reserve has provided a more secure situation, readily accepted by the geese and by Coot. Most of the Coot (about eight pairs) and the occasional Moorhen nest in the rushes and willows that fringe the lake. Egyptian Geese are feral breeders and nest on occasion, in an old Crow's or Buzzard's nest, often at a considerable height. The only resident duck, the Mallard, finds suitable nesting sites, often in the cover of the woodland trees. Tufted Duck may also be seen; some non-breeders will summer.

Away from the water the diversity of the habitats surrounding the lake provides an abundance of nesting sites. Birds of prey are represented by two or three pairs of Buzzard, and by Kestrel and Sparrowhawk in most years. Tawny Owls find convenient holes in old trees, as do Stock Doves, which have also nested under the main road bridge. All three woodpeckers are present, the Great Spotted by far the most frequent and occurring in all suitable woods. In the mature oakwoods the Wood Warbler is a common summer resident, and the Pied Flycatcher, encouraged by the provision of nestboxes, has steadily increased, with up to 30 pairs each year. Thorn scrub,

bramble thickets and other thick undergrowth attract Blackcap, Garden
Warbler and Whitethroat in good numbers. The Whinchats, which colonised
almost every tree-plot during the first few years after planting, have now
joined the Skylarks and Meadow Pipits in less disturbed places as the
recreational popularity of the area has increased. Among the 67 species of
birds that have been recorded as breeding since 1978 can be included Raven,
Tree Pipit, Grey Wagtail, Stonechat and Willow Tit, with Wheatear in the
rocks beside the bridge and Dipper in a drainpipe near the dam.

Nearby forestry plantations attract parties of Redpolls and occasionally
Crossbills. In the winter, Redpolls and Siskins will feed in the woodlands in
the birch trees and scrub.

Wimbleball is still a developing site. Some of the habitats around the lake
are gradually changing, affected by various management work, particularly in
the nature reserve. The creation of this large freshwater habitat has become a
great asset to the National Park, enriching the area by its attraction of
additional species of birds, with wintering wildfowl, passage-migrants and
breeders.

Roger Butcher

EXMOOR

Today the moorland areas of the Exmoor National Park cover about
16,200ha, having been 30,400ha at the beginning of this century. With the
watching brief and powers of the National Park Authority, there is unlikely to
be any major change of the surviving moorlands in the near future. These are
almost equally divided between heather and grass, with most lying between
300 and 500m above sea level. The grass moors cover much of the ancient
Royal Forest and lie in the south-western half of the moor. To the north and
east are the heather moors, many of them open commons or National Trust
land.

The annual rainfall on The Chains running north-west of Simonsbath
averages over 230cm, and here, 460m up, are the head-waters of the Rivers
Barle, Exe, Bray and West Lyn, and of Farley and Hoaroak Waters. The
Horner, Avill and Quarme rise on the slopes of Dunkery, and in common
with the Somerset sections of the other waters are well-bordered with
oakwoods. These form a fine habitat for woodland and waterside birds, as
well as regular harbouring quarters for the wild Red Deer.

The long-threatened demise of the Black Grouse occurred in the late
1970s; the last cock bird was recorded in 1975, and the last hen in 1981. It

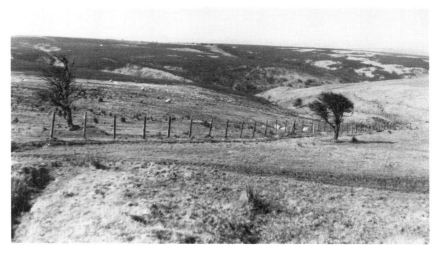

Lucott Moor, Exmoor

seems the Red Grouse (an introduced species) is also on the way out, with only two or three pairs hanging on around Dunkery Beacon. Birds of prey continue to do well on the moor, some breeding and others overflying in search of food. The beech shelter-belts planted around 130 years ago are favourite nesting sites for Buzzards; Sparrowhawks occasionally use isolated pines, and Kestrels old Crows' nests. Two to five pairs of Merlins breed annually with varying success, and the Hobby may well have nested over the last two years. Ravens often nest in moorland beeches, and though the Peregrine does not breed away from the coast it is often seen over the high ground inland. Autumn to spring visitors include the Hen Harrier and Great Grey Shrike, and less regularly the Red Kite, Marsh and Montagu's Harriers. Snow Buntings and Dotterel are fairly regular migrants over the moor.

Wheatears and Ring Ouzels are invariably back on Exmoor by the end of March, followed three weeks later by Whinchats and Redstarts. These all now breed in bigger numbers than 20 years ago, particularly in the combes of the northern moors from Dunkery to Brendon Common (in Devon). Stonechats remain fairly common, nesting in sheltered combes along the coast, but much depends on them getting through the winters. The Cuckoo is usually back calling on the moor by 20 April, and is still quite a common bird here, with Meadow and Tree Pipits the chief hosts.

Curlew and Snipe continue to nest on the moor, but both may have

Horner wood

declined. Some other birds which breed regularly in a moorland habitat
include the Reed Bunting, Skylark, Linnet, Wren, Mistle Thrush, Chaf-
finch, and Carrion Crow.

There are rookeries above 300m at Simonsbath and Warren Farm, and the
heronry off Badgworthy Water is surrounded by heather moorland. In 1983,
a Song Thrush nested successfully in heather at 460m on Dunkery, and in
1987 a Pheasant was covering four young on the top of Ley Hill. Yellowhammers and Redpoll breed on the fringes of the moor, often in gorse near
Webber's Post and on Haddon Hill.

Exmoor has almost 500km of rivers and streams, the fast-running waters
attractive to Dippers and Grey Wagtails, both of which remain common.
The Pied Wagtail is a much more cosmopolitan nester. Kingfishers have
always been scarce in west Somerset but there is evidence of some increase;
a pair or two breed fairly regularly on the lower sections of the Exe around
Winsford and Dulverton and occasionally on the Avill above Dunster. In
the autumn and winter they scatter along the Barle as far up as Simonsbath
and down to the coast at Minehead and Porlock. Common Sandpipers

appear on passage every spring, usually single birds, with family parties in autumn, but there are no recent breeding records. Smaller numbers of Green Sandpipers travel along the streams as do Wood Sandpipers, though much less frequently.

Grey Herons in the Exmoor area have doubled in numbers over the past 20 years to about 35 nesting pairs. There are now several small heronries, the most recent at Badgworthy Deer Park. At 335m up it is certainly the highest in Somerset and perhaps in England. Mallard nest along many streams, even as high up as 400m on The Meads, the source of Chalk Water. The Reed Bunting has a similar nesting range from the coastal marshes to rushy patches by moorland springs.

During the 1970s, three to six pairs of Sand Martins nested at each of four sites within the Exmoor National Park: Roadwater, Dunster, Exford and Landacre Bridge. All these sites have been deserted, partly due to erosion of banks, partly to disturbance, but mainly no doubt to the general decline of this bird over much of Britain. However, in 1987, three pairs did nest near the Barle-Exe junction below Dulverton, and passage birds are still seen each spring, but in much smaller numbers.

Over recent years there has been little change in the wooded parts of Exmoor, which cover 6700ha. About 2025ha are considered 'ancient' woodland and consist largely of oaks with a rich variety of lichens and insects. The largest single block is the 365ha Horner Wood owned by the National Trust; this is a major bird habitat. Equally important are the wooded parts of Hawkcombe, Avill, Exe and Barle Valleys. Crossbills are often recorded in conifers from various parts of Exmoor, and there is evidence of breeding, with reports of juveniles.

Among the woodpeckers, the Green is probably the most common, but the Great Spotted has increased and is now running a close second. It frequently comes to garden bird-tables to feed, and often brings its young as well. The Lesser Spotted is certainly now more widespread, but does remain the scarcest. The Nuthatch, another bird-table feeder, and the Treecreeper have at least maintained their numbers and do not seem greatly affected by hard winters. On the other hand the Goldcrest suffers badly and takes some years to recover. Firecrests are now regularly recorded as late autumn or winter visitors, mainly in the Dunster to Minehead districts. Siskins bred near Luccombe in 1979, the first recorded nesting in Somerset, and a few pairs have probably bred in most years since.

The Tawny Owl is by far the commonest owl on Exmoor and nests in many woods, and in 1987 bred successfully in Blenheim Gardens in the middle of Minehead. Little Owls are still scarce, and Barn Owls are now down to a few pairs at the most. Buzzards have fully recovered from their heavy losses in the late 1950s and can be seen from the coast to the high moor.

Webber's Post

The Sparrowhawk, too, is now back to good numbers and regularly takes birds from gardens, and the Kestrel has shown some increase over the years.

Summer visitors to Exmoor's woods and thickets have mostly done well in recent years. There have been some ups and downs with Whitethroats, Spotted Flycatchers, and Chiffchaffs, but Pied Flycatchers, Redstarts and Wood Warblers have all increased. Pied Flycatchers have gone up from about 30 pairs in 1968 to well over 100 in 1987. They have been helped by nestboxes put up in a number of woods, though more than half of these have been taken over by Blue Tits. Blackcaps and Garden Warblers are common, but the Willow is the most abundant warbler.

Noel Allen

THE COAST FROM HINKLEY POINT
TO THE DEVON BORDER

The coastline from Hinkley to Watchet is a curiously melancholy place, with low, crumbling cliffs of lias, a muddy beach, and a sea more often brown than blue. It has few birds except Rock Pipits, though Herring Gulls breed when the population levels are high. Most of the wintering waders are Turnstones and Oystercatchers. The most exciting event that ever happened along here was the execution of an Egyptian Vulture at Kilve in 1825! At the outflow of Doniford Brook, just east of Watchet, there is a winter gull-roost and a few ducks winter here; there is also an intermittent Sand Martin colony. There are some Purple Sandpiper records from Watchet Harbour. The coastal path along the cliff-top to Blue Anchor passes through woodland and undercliff which are good for warblers, Stock Doves and Yellowhammers. This has long been known as the north-west extremity of the Nightingale's distribution in Somerset. Cirl Buntings may survive on the landward slopes behind the ridge.

From Blue Anchor to Minehead Harbour the foreshore is more interesting, with a fair variety of winter and passage waders on the mixed sand and pebble beach, though this is, of course, much disturbed. The chalet camp at Dunster Beach is placed between the beach and the old, silted-up harbour, The Hawen. The wood here regularly holds wintering Chiffchaffs and Firecrests, and attracts other passing migrants. Beyond it, the little that is left of Minehead Marshes, drastically disturbed and much diminished in recent years, no longer holds the once-regular flock of White-fronted Geese. The building in 1961 of Butlin's Camp (now 'Somerwest World') drained most of the area, but several new ponds created within have helped to sustain the largest flock of Canada Geese in Somerset, who commute between here and the Brendon Hills reservoirs.

Beyond Minehead Harbour the isolated massif of the North Hill/Selworthy Ridge towers up, falls then steeply and almost inaccessibly to the sea until the sheer cliffs of Hurlstone Point are reached. Ravens breed here, and so do Shelduck, Wheatears and Rock Pipits on the landslips, but the former colony of Herring Gulls is at present almost deserted. In their 'boom' years, Stonechats are common, but the moorland summit of the ridge is too disturbed to be of much interest except for passing migrants. The south-facing inward slope above Selworthy and Bossington was planted by the Acland family in the eighteenth century with a great diversity of trees, including a large but now decaying ilex wood.

Between Hurlstone and Porlock Weir lies the great shingle sweep of

Porlock Bay, backed at its western end by Porlock Marsh. This is the remaining fragment of a once-larger flooded area containing the biggest duck-decoy in Somerset. It still has a reed-bed and a variable amount of open water, but it is so much walked and (in winter) shot over that it promises more in the way of birds than it delivers. This is the only west Somerset breeding place of Redshank; there are small numbers of waders and wintering duck, and over the years many rarities have been seen.

Hurlestone Point and Porlock Bay

The coast west of Porlock Weir is one of the strangest places in Somerset, accessible only at low tide along the forbidding boulder beach or by two paths from above. The hanging woods are part natural, part planted by the Hallidays, who built the house of Glenthorne just over the Devon border. Much woodland is choked by rhododendron. Two small rock-faces have erratic Herring Gull colonies, and Shelduck also breed. The cliff at Glenthorne has since 1981 held the only Fulmar colony in Somerset.

Although more interest has been taken in sea-watching in recent years, there is often little to see offshore along the western part of the coast, where numbers are often dependent on the wind and on the timing and state of the tidal flow. From spring to autumn, Gannets, Fulmars and Manx Shearwaters occur more or less regularly, as do Razorbills and Guillemots, but they may be far out to sea. A north-west wind, especially overnight, brings more birds up Channel and drives them nearer to land; large-scale movements of Kittiwakes sometimes occur in winter, as they struggle to get back out to sea. Shags, terns, skuas, petrels and phalaropes can also be seen, especially after autumn gales. A small number of Red-throated Divers winter offshore.

David Ballance

Specific List

This list contains all species and subspecies known to have occurred in the 'new' county of Somerset since 1800. For details of records before 1966, including evidence from palaeontology, see Palmer and Ballance (1968), which also has a full bibliography of earlier material.

Classification and nomenclature largely follow K.H. Voous (1977) in *List of Recent Holarctic Bird Species*, with later emendments.

Most doubtful records have been excluded; we have generally followed the decisions of the *British Birds* Rarities Committee, but we have felt free to differ from them on one or two records. All records known to us up to the end of 1987 have been included, and species' totals are up to the end of that year unless indicated otherwise. A small number of significant records up to August 1988 have also been included, and are clearly dated. Pending records and those awaiting acceptance by the *British Birds* Rarities Committee are listed in the Appendix (p. 238).

This List has been based almost entirely on an analysis of records printed in *The Report on Somerset Birds* (abbreviated to *RSB*). No acknowledgements are made to this, and space has prevented the inclusion of observers' names. All recent county ornithologies must owe a great debt to the two national Bird Atlases. These are:

SHARROCK, J.T.R.: *The Atlas of Breeding Birds in Britain and Ireland* (for the BTO and the Irish Wildbird Conservancy) 1976 (based on fieldwork carried out from 1968 to 1972).
LACK, P.: *The Atlas of Wintering Birds in Britain and Ireland* (for the same bodies) 1986 (based on fieldwork from 1980 to 1984).

We have quoted them frequently, especially for the distribution of passerines, and they are abbreviated as *Breeding Atlas* and *Winter Atlas*.

Place-names follow the usage of the Ordnance Survey (with occasional local variations) and may be found by reference to the Gazetteer (p. 251) and the Map (p. 250). Certain general areas need definition here. The Levels of the Central Somerset Plain are divided thus: the North Levels are those between the Mendip Hills and the Poldens, including the heathland area known as the peat-moors; the Central Levels are those from the Poldens south to a line drawn between Somerton and North Curry; and the South Levels are those south of Langport. Except for the last, the usage here differs from that sometimes employed in the older literature, including Palmer and Ballance, when the Gordano Levels, now in Avon, were called the North Levels, and the Central block included everything between the Mendips and Langport.

Records for the county of Avon are not included, but a few well-known sites, such as the Axe Estuary, are divided by the new county boundary, and records from these do, of course, appear.

The holiday camp at Minehead is now called Somerwest World, but it was founded as Butlin's, and it still bears that name locally, so we thought it less confusing to keep it.

A number of shorter papers which we have used are referred to in the usual way, and are listed alphabetically in the Bibliography (p. 242).

Divers   *Gavia sp.*

The status of all three species off the Somerset coast is uncertain. Patient observation with good optics might well establish them as more regular than published records show, but they often appear in poor visibility at the extreme limit of identification range. Two recent day-counts of 16 and 20 divers off Hurlstone Point, in January and February 1988, are perhaps a more accurate reflection of their numbers. Red-throated Divers regularly winter off the Devon coast, and probably account for many of those not specifically identified off Somerset.

Red-throated Diver   *Gavia stellata*

Winter visitor and passage-migrant; scarce, but probably regular.

Six were recorded before 1912, and there have been at least 95 since, with an average of two a year since 1966. Half of these have been on the coast of Bridgwater Bay or west of Blue Anchor, with the rest on the larger inland waters. Mostly early November to early March, especially January and February. Others on spring passage from April to June; once each in August and September. Singly or in twos, except for five off Brean Down, 29 April 1975.

Black-throated Diver   *Gavia arctica*

Winter visitor; very rare.

Since 1875, about 23 have occurred on the coast and at the reservoirs. Twelve of these have been since 1964: nine at Cheddar Reservoir, and others off the coast or at Wimbleball. Singly, apart from three records of two together. All from late October to late March, and mostly from November to February.

Great Northern Diver   *Gavia immer*

Winter visitor and passage-migrant; rare.

About 60 on the coasts and inland waters since 1912, of which 25 have been since 1966. Almost all recent birds have been on the coast or at Cheddar Reservoir, where they have sometimes remained for up to four months. Apart from two April records and one bird in August, all have been from November to March, and most in December and January.

Little Grebe   *Tachybaptus ruficollis*

Resident, summer visitor and passage-migrant; locally common.

Although it may occasionally breed on slow-flowing rivers such as the Frome and Tone, the Dabchick has in Somerset been largely dependent on man's provision of water: first of park-lakes, then of clay- and gravel-pits, and later of reservoirs. Its lack of glamour has certainly caused it to be under-recorded by modern bird-watchers; it is more widespread on smaller waters than the published records show. Breeding success is often dependent on water levels.

It breeds on most large and small waters with adequate cover, though seldom on higher ground. There are few breeding records from the west, though it has bred at Dunster Hawen and on some newly created ponds between the Brendons and the sea. From August to March, smaller waters are often deserted. Autumn gatherings occur on reservoirs, especially at Durleigh and Sutton Bingham, where up to 40 are regular and up to 65 have been reported, but numbers are not maintained after October, when they emigrate. In hard weather, they may visit the coast of Bridgwater Bay and the larger rivers. An exceptional record, apparently unconnected with frost, was of 17 in the Brue Estuary, 26 November 1985.

Great Crested Grebe   *Podiceps cristatus*

Resident, summer and winter visitor and passage-migrant; locally common.

In the last century this decorative bird was rare in Somerset; it was no doubt persecuted, but there were few suitable breeding waters other than a few heavily 'preserved' park lakes. It returned to breed at Chard Reservoir in 1910 and gradually spread to other waters.

The spring population might seem high to an observer visiting suitable

reservoirs and pits in April, but breeding success has always been erratic, since it is dependent on food-supply, lack of disturbance from fishing and boating, and the tolerance of predators and competitors, such as Mink or Mute Swan; the maintenance of water levels is often an even more important factor. Thus, in 1982 birds were present on at least a dozen waters, but no successful breeding took place. Sites where birds have bred with some regularity include: Orchardleigh Lake; Durleigh, Chard and Sutton Bingham Reservoirs; most of the larger clay-pits in the Bridgwater and Highbridge area; and several flooded peat-workings on the North Levels. Persistent attempts to colonise Wimbleball Reservoir succeeded only in 1985, when one pair brought off young; this was the first breeding record for anywhere west of the Quantocks.

Except in hard weather some birds are resident on breeding waters, but most leave in summer or late autumn to gather on major reservoirs, where there may have been non-breeders also in the summer. The highest numbers are usually at Cheddar: up to 40 fairly regularly, exceptionally 113 (January 1979). A few appear on the coast or on flood-waters from autumn to spring.

Red-necked Grebe *Podiceps grisegena*

Winter visitor; very rare.

Our rarest grebe. Eleven were recorded from 1870 to 1965, and there have been 13 since, including two together at Cheddar Reservoir, January 1982.

Almost all at major reservoirs, especially Cheddar, with odd birds on flooded levels, in Bridgwater Bay or at Porlock Marsh; December to April, with three in October and single records for September and November.

Slavonian Grebe   *Podiceps auritus*

Winter visitor and passage-migrant; very scarce.

About 69 have been recorded since 1900; 34 since 1966. All but 11 of recent birds have been at Cheddar Reservoir; others were in Bridgwater Bay, on inland floods, at Sutton Bingham, Dunster Hawen, and once off Brean Down. About 70 per cent occurred from November to January, and there have been no records from mid-May to mid-August.

Black-necked Grebe   *Podiceps nigricollis*

Passage-migrant; rare. Has bred.

A pair bred at Orchardleigh in 1932; birds were present on the lake in 1931 and 1933, and there was a pair at Cheddar Reservoir in 1941.

About 83 have been seen since 1914, but only 25 of these since 1966. Recorded from late July to late November and from early January to early May, so that those that do reach us are stray birds on passage rather than winter visitors. Almost all recent ones have been at Cheddar, Durleigh and Sutton Bingham Reservoirs, with odd ones on other waters and at Porlock Marsh. Most move on quickly, though a few have stayed for up to a month.

Fulmar   *Fulmarus glacialis*

Summer visitor and passage-migrant; local on coasts. One breeding colony.

From 1869 to 1950 a rare storm-vagrant; only about seven recorded, all in autumn and winter. From 1951, a slow increase began in the Bristol Channel: on the Devon side of Exmoor, they bred at Martinhoe in 1955, and by 1965 were appearing annually, especially off Brean Down and west of Minehead. There were 282 pairs on the North Devon coast from Lynton to Haddon's Mouth in 1987. About three times as many were seen in the Channel from 1972 to 1977 as had been seen from 1966 to 1971; that rate of increase has not been maintained, but patient sea-watchers have been able to see them fairly regularly in Bridgwater Bay and off the west coast, often during north-west winds. The combination of these with high tides account for many sightings. Up to ten have been seen together, and during sea-watches it is often hard to estimate total numbers. Higher numbers have been recorded in gales: 120, Porlock Bay, 25 July 1977; 97 off Brean Down, 26 August 1986; and on the same day about 500 in Blue Anchor Bay. Most are recorded from early March to early September; only about 17 records of live birds from October to February, when a few others have been found dead.

In 1972, three were seen prospecting the cliff to the east of Glenthorne, and a pair was present there in 1974, but breeding was not proved till 1981; there have been up to five pairs since. In spring, odd birds regularly prospect the cliffs on the south side of Brean Down, and in 1986 and 1987, a pair prospected Culver Cliff at Minehead.

Inland, five records of storm-vagrants since 1966, including one gliding from east to west over Nynehead, 3 January 1977.

One ringed on Canna, Inner Hebrides, April 1974, was found dead at Berrow, 1982.

Cory's Shearwater   *Calonectris diomedea*

Vagrant.

Four records: single birds in the Parrett Estuary, 11 and 19 September 1983; three to south, Berrow, 26 August 1986; one down-Channel off Minehead, 6 September 1987.

Sooty Shearwater   *Puffinus griseus*

Vagrant.

Eight records: one off Brean Down, 19 June 1971; one, Porlock Bay, 23 September 1972; seven off Minehead, 9 August 1979; one, Steart, 18

September 1983; two off Berrow, 2 August 1986, and another there later on the same evening; one off Kilve, 29 August 1986; one down-Channel, Porlock Bay, 2 August 1987.

Manx Shearwater   *Puffinus puffinus*

Atlantic race *P. p. puffinus*
Non-breeding summer visitor and passage-migrant; local on coasts.

Small parties are regular in the Bristol Channel from early or mid-May to mid-September; occasional April and October records. The largest numbers are generally from late May to mid-July; most of these are probably birds from the Dyfed breeding colonies. Many are seen during strong winds from the west or north-west, but in view of records of several hundred off Porlock and in the Bridgwater Bay on early midsummer mornings (and regular sightings from Steep Holm), they must make regular feeding flights up-Channel at dawn, though they may be too far offshore to be seen. There have been some 40 records of 100 or more, and 3 of 1000: Brean Down, 19 July 1972; Porlock Bay, 5 June 1977 and in July 1988. September birds are perhaps mainly wind-blown vagrants; a juvenile found at Steart, 15 September 1966, had been ringed at Skokholm on the 5th.

In recent years, 4 found inland: Frome, 21 October 1973; injured birds at Taunton and Shepton Mallet after gales in early September 1983, and 1, Cheddar Reservoir, 2 September 1988.

West Mediterranean race *P.p. mauretanicus*

Vagrant.

Two records: two, Minehead, 1 June 1958; one, Hinkley Point, 15 September 1985.

Storm Petrel   *Hydrobates pelagicus*

Storm-vagrant, mainly in autumn.

At least 85 have been seen since 1850, of which 50 have been since 1966. They probably occur more regularly far offshore, as half the recent records have been from ships. Mostly June to September, occasionally October to January. Petrels close to shore may be at risk from other dangers than wind: off Brean Down, one was taken by a Herring Gull, 27 May 1972, and others by Peregrines, 24 August 1985 and 7 August 1986. All recent records have been coastal, except one on Cheddar Reservoir, 3 September 1983, and two found in Taunton, around the same time.

Leach's Petrel   *Oceanodroma leucorhoa*

Storm-vagrant, mainly in autumn and early winter.

Because of 'wrecks', more Leach's than Storm Petrels have been seen in Somerset. Much the largest of these was in 1952, when more than 2100 were seen between 23 October and 9 November, about half being found dead; these included 120 inland, of which 50 to 60 were at Cheddar Reservoir. Despite this, Leach's are less regular than Storm. Since 1967, they have occurred in only ten years, with a total of about 69 birds, all between 3 September and 15 January. Most of them have been along the east coast of Bridgwater Bay, with two in Porlock Bay and three at Cheddar Reservoir. There are two spring/summer records: Porlock Bay, 7 May 1928; Steart, 1 June 1972.

Gannet   *Sula bassana*

Summer visitor and passage-migrant; local.

Before the 1950s, when little sea-watching was done, there was no clear pattern in the offshore records. Since then, found to be regular in small numbers from April to September along the coast. Most keep well out to sea, but can be seen at a greater distance than any other seabird. The Grassholm colony has increased greatly since the 1940s, and is the likely source of most adults. Gannets are most likely to be seen off Brean Down and the coast west of Watchet, in strong north-west or west winds, but odd birds are often off the west coast even in calm weather, especially early in the day. They are much commoner in some years than in others, presumably because of the distribution of shoals of fish; in 1966 birds were regularly fishing for mackerel in Porlock Bay.

Most records are of fewer than ten birds, but counts of up to 30 or 40 are not unusual, especially in the west, and much higher numbers have been seen in gales: 130, Porlock Bay, 3 September 1967; 70 there, 7 August 1986; 100, Brean Down, 25 July 1971.

Rare from October to March; mostly adults in winter storms.   About 16 have been blown inland since 1965, six of these at various sites in north and central Somerset in early September 1983.

Cormorant   *Phalacrocorax carbo*

Passage-migrant, winter visitor and non-breeding summer visitor; local.

Very scarce in the nineteenth century, because of persecution and lack of suitable inland waters. Gradually increased, and first bred on Steep Holm (now Avon) in 1934. Many records in north Somerset are due to this colony, which also serves as a winter roost. Wintering has on the whole been more common since the 1950s.

Well distributed from late summer to spring on levels, at major reservoirs and along the coast, especially in Bridgwater Bay and west of Dunster; the nearest north Devon colony is now near Combe Martin. Up to 50 have been seen flying to and from Steep Holm and rather smaller numbers in winter at reservoirs, especially Cheddar and Wimbleball. Shooting by the Water Authority at the latter has led to the recovery of birds ringed on the Solway, on the Dyfed coast and in Ulster; other colour-ringed Dyfed birds have been seen at Sutton Bingham, and one was shot at East Coker in 1986; there were earlier recoveries from the Isle of Man and from Anglesey. Odd birds turn up almost anywhere in the county, in flight, on rivers and on park-lakes, especially in autumn, and a few non-breeders summer on the coast.

Often seen flying inland following rivers and, since 1974, many have taken to perching on the wires and electricity pylons where they cross such watercourses on the levels. The largest gatherings have been over Chilton Moor and Lang Moor, where up to 32 have been counted.

Shag *Phalacrocorax aristotelis*

Occasional visitor, mainly to the coasts in autumn.

About 47 birds between 1870 and 1965, and 75 records since. Almost all off the rockier parts of the coast, at Brean Down or west of Minehead, with a few at the reservoirs, and occasional wind-blown vagrants in odd places, such as on a cowshed roof at Fiddington, 18 February 1972. Generally ones and twos, but two recent records of flocks of immatures: 22, Brean Down, 17 August 1979; 49, Porlock Bay, 5 September 1980. Recorded in all months, but more than half have been in August or September.

Bittern *Botaurus stellaris*

Winter visitor and passage-migrant; very rare. May have bred.

Booming was heard on the South Levels in 1952 and in nine summers near Bridgwater between 1958 and 1977, when there were also two records of twos and threes flushed from clay-pits in September or October, too early for the normal pattern of winter visitors. A very young bird was picked up on the M5 in the early 1970s.

A few Bitterns probably visit Somerset every winter; they were more often seen or shot in the old days when guns and dogs covered every marsh. About 28 have been seen or found dead since 1966, and since 1977 there have been annual winter records from late November to February (mostly in January). None in March, but two recently in April. Most records are from clay-pits, the levels and Minehead and Porlock Marshes.

American Bittern   *Botaurus lentiginosus*

Vagrant.

Two records: Long Sutton, winter 1898; Catcott (remains only), 26 May 1928.

Little Bittern   *Ixobrychus minutus*

Vagrant; has summered.

Four old records: Taunton, 20 August 1860; Glastonbury, about 1860; Langport, October 1862 or 1864; Kingston St Mary, before 1911.

At Huntworth, males were seen in summer from 1958 to 1960 and a bird thought to be an adult female in July and August 1958. Birds summered at two places in this area, 1970.

Night Heron   *Nycticorax nycticorax*

Vagrant.

Five records: near Bridgwater, before 1858; North Moor, Godney, about 1872; Street, 1876; Bathpool, 12 June 1912; Three Bridges, Nynehead, 16 May and 11 June 1972.

Squacco Heron   *Ardeola ralloides*

Vagrant.

One very old record: a female near Bridgwater, spring or early September 1825.

Cattle Egret   *Bubulcus ibis*

Vagrant.

One certain record: one at various places in the East Coker/Sutton Bingham/ Key Bridge area, December 1985. It remained into 1986; on 23 February it was captured and tended at West Hatch by the RSPCA during the very cold weather. Released on West Sedge Moor, it was last seen near Othery and Middlezoy, 18 March to 18 April.

Little Egret   *Egretta garzetta*

Vagrant.

The seven recent records suggest overshoots on spring passage in a species which has extended its range northwards in France: Axe Estuary, 22 May 1965; Wall Common, 9–13 May 1968; Axe Estuary, 28 August 1968; Porlock Marsh, 14 May 1979; South Moor, Glastonbury, 31 May 1983; Steart, 1 June 1984, and another bird on Steart Island, 21 August.

Grey Heron   *Ardea cinerea*

Resident, passage-migrant and winter visitor; locally common.

In 1987 there were 16 heronries in Somerset, with a total of about 190 occupied nests. The largest colonies have always been in woods or copses on the levels or around their edge; a further 30 nests were on Exmoor. The history and present state of the colonies are summarised thus:

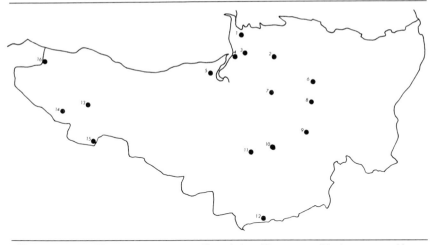

No. (see map)	Heronry	Founded	Nests 1987	Maximum recorded	Notes
1	Lympsham	1979	5	8 (1985)	
2	Tadham Moor	1941	c.15	40 (1977)	(a)
3	Somerset Court, Brent Knoll	1956	4	25 (1979)	
4	West Huntspill Churchyard	1982	1	4 (1984/85)	
5	Hill House, Otterhampton	1952	14	19 (1983-85)	
6	Queen's Sedge Moor	1971	8	10 (1976/77)	
7	Purchase Copse, Shapwick	1964	7	33 (1977)	(b)
8	Moorhouse, R. Brue (up to seven at Butleigh Court until 1986)	1986	4	4 (1987)	
9	Somerton Erleigh	pre-1870	11	116 (1952)	
10	Washams Wood, Midelney Manor	1925	14	42 (1954)	
11	Swell Wood	pre-1902	72	80 (1986)	
12	Wayford Manor	c.1966	6	11 (1983)	
13	Coppleham Cross, Winsford	pre-1965	10	28 (1971)	
14	Hayes Wood, Withypool	c.1976	6	8 (1984)	
15	Hele Manor, Exebridge	c.1974	3	14 (1982/83)	
16	Badgworthy Deer Park	pre-1984	11	12 (1984)	

Notes:
(a) Fluctuating numbers; counting has sometimes been difficult.
(b) Formerly at Ice House Copse, Shapwick

Other sites used by odd pairs since 1975 have been at Stolford, Ham (Creech St Michael), Leigh Woods (Blagdon Hill), Sandhill Park (Bishop's Lydeard), Durleigh Reservoir, Porlock Marsh and Oareford. There seems to have been no breeding in east Somerset since the extinction of a small colony in Marston Park in 1958. The history of colonies in the west was not well documented until recently. Among large heronries now extinct (generally because of tree-felling) may be mentioned those at Halswell Park (1856–1963), Knowle Hill, Dunster (1857–1912), and Aller's Wood, Dulverton (1831–1962).

Despite pollution, drainage and cold winters, there are now more breeding birds than in 1966, when 124 nests were counted, though this may have been an underestimate. From then to 1977 there was a steady increase to 292; since then numbers have fluctuated, the worst year being 1987.

Colonies are occupied from late winter to June or July. From late summer to autumn birds arrive from eastern England and the Continent, some of which may stay to winter, and in colder weather Scandinavian birds may arrive. Late-summer gatherings of up to 40 have been found in reed-beds and major reservoirs. Most breeders are probably resident, though juveniles may wander. In some recent years many must have emigrated, and those that remained suffered severely in the cold spells: six were found dead at Catcott in February 1986.

Nocturnal feeding aided by street-lighting was noted at Puriton, 1975–76.

Purple Heron   *Ardea purpurea*

Vagrant.

Three records: Godney Moor, 24 May 1977; an adult, Westhay Moor, 16 April 1979; Sutton Bingham Reservoir, 13 May 1982.

White Stork   *Ciconia ciconia*

Vagrant.

Four records in all.

On 9 September 1971, three ringed juveniles arrived at Combe Down (now in Avon). The next day they moved to Downside School, where one fell down the chimney and was taken to Rode Bird Gardens. The other two were later seen at Nettlebridge, and in Cornwall; one of them reached Madeira on 21 September. All had been ringed at one nest in North Jutland, Denmark, on 6 September. The Rode bird was released in early September 1972, and this was presumably the bird seen at Huntworth on 25 and 26 September; one over Rode, 14 July, was a different bird.

The other records were: one, Witcombe, near Ash, 28 February 1976; an adult, Westhay Heath and neighbourhood, 29 June–19 July 1986.

Black Stork   *Ciconia nigra*

Vagrant.

One very old record: a bird caught alive on West Sedge Moor, 13 May 1814.

Glossy Ibis   *Plegadis falcinellus*

Vagrant.

Four records: Shapwick, 1859; Brean, November 1920; Cannington, early December 1921; Templecombe, 28 August 1977.

Spoonbill   *Platalea leucorodia*

Passage-migrant and summer visitor; very rare.

Two old records of birds on West Sedge Moor, 1813, and on Curry Moor, before 1853. About 24 from 1944 to 1983, in ones and twos, except for a party of five near Ilchester, 6 April 1964. Most recent birds have been seen in flight, in a surprising variety of places, both coastal and inland. Mostly from April to June; no records from January to March.

A NOTE ON WILDFOWL

There are two general problems with regard to the increasing number of escaped birds and introduced species.

The first concerns species which might occur in the wild, such as Barnacle and Greylag Geese and Red-crested Pochard, but which are known to be kept in collections in Somerset and elsewhere. Some escapes are clearly recognisable by tameness, or by occurring at odd places and times; others can seem quite wild, perhaps associating with wild birds of other species, so no-one can know whether they really are. Small private collections of birds such as Red-breasted Geese, Ruddy Shelduck and Cape Shoveler are known to be kept on ponds on the Mendips, so the validity of records of birds like Marbled Teal and White-headed Duck in the area is still under discussion by national record committees. The close proximity of renowned collections like Slimbridge with its many free-winged species clouds the issue still further.

The second problem is of exotic species which have originally been introduced, yet ultimately persist in the wild without human support, and often in places away from their original introduction, like Canada and Egyptian Geese and Ruddy Duck. These are simpler to deal with, though the point at which they should be regarded as wild birds may be hard to define.

There are no golden rules, and in practice each species presents its own individual problem.

Mute Swan   *Cygnus olor*

Resident, summer and winter visitor; locally common.

There are records back to 1247. In 1420, birds were taken on Porlock Marsh, and the Abbot of Glastonbury and later the Luttrell family of Dunster Castle owned swans on Meare Pool; the latter's marks are recorded.

They bred widely on park-lakes and rivers before 1900. The increase of suitable waters in this century has been to their advantage, though it has to some extent been counterbalanced by the effects of pollution, especially by lead; by casualties from overhead wires; and by local persecution of a casual kind, since both they and their nests offer tempting targets. A BTO Census of 1955 found 126 nests and 153 non-breeders in the old county; by contrast, a similar count in 1983 found 89 breeding pairs and 353 or more non-breeders in the new county. Since south Avon contains two major reservoirs and some minor waters, together with some suitable rivers, there has probably been little change in the breeding population of the new county, and a great increase in the number of summering birds, though the 1955 figures were then thought too low. Furthermore, the 1983 Census was incomplete, excluding some suitable waters in east and south-west Somerset. Breeding is very largely confined to the levels, with outliers on some park lakes, reservoirs and pits. West of the Quantocks breeds only at Dunster Hawen/ Minehead Marshes (up to three pairs); has bred Porlock Marsh, but not for some years. Breeds irregularly in the south-west (for example, around Wellington) and on park lakes and the River Frome in the east.

In autumn, birds tend to congregate on reservoirs (Cheddar, Durleigh, Sutton Bingham) but numbers here have been lower since about 1980, with no more than an average of 10 to 15 on each water. By contrast, recent numbers on Tealham Moor have increased, with a record count of 105 there in October 1982. Some birds evidently go to moult at the Abbotsbury Swannery in Dorset, and either winter there or return north to the levels after their moult. In mild winters, some remain on their breeding waters, for example at Dunster Hawen, but most gather in herds on the levels. The areas they frequent and their numbers vary greatly from year to year. North of the Poldens, herds of up to 120 may be found on Tealham Moor and (recently) on the South Drain near Catcott and on Westhay Moor. To the south, larger numbers often occur, on King's Sedge Moor, on West Sedge Moor and the South Levels; up to 150 have been recorded in each area. In most years, these herds are fragmented, moving in small groups over different moors. The large population of non-breeders recorded in the 1983 Census was concentrated on levels both sides of the Poldens.

Recent low water levels on the streams and rivers around Cheddar have concentrated the natural lead deposits in the water, and at least three Mute Swans were found poisoned in the first three months of 1988.

Bewick's Swan   *Cygnus columbianus*

Winter visitor; local and scarce.

In the last century, a rare visitor in hard weather. Not certainly recorded between 1891 and 1937, and only about eight January–March records from then till 1950, from reservoirs and levels. Annual from 1950 to 1954, in small numbers. In the winter of 1954/55, however, they suddenly began to increase, so that by 1968/69 there were 110 and the following year 208. This was at a time of a general increase in England. In the 1950s, extensive winter flooding was normal on King's Sedge Moor and the South Levels. As this became less regular, the herd, which fed together or in scattered groups on many moors south of the Poldens, began to roost at the reservoirs, especially Durleigh; Sutton Bingham has been used more erratically. This habit has continued.

Numbers have never dropped below 100 since 1968, and at their highest have generally been between 130 and 200. Occasionally they have gone much higher, especially late in the winter: 386 were on King's Moor and West Sedge Moor, 10 February 1974; 380 on Wet Moor, 1 January 1982; and 384 flew in to roost at Durleigh, 3 February 1985.

A few come in November (exceptionally as early as 17 October) but the main arrival in most years is in early December. The first often arrive in small parties, at the reservoirs or on the coast of Bridgwater Bay, later moving to feed on the levels for the middle of the winter. In recent years the highest numbers have been found on Wet Moor, West Sedge Moor, Curry Moor and Penzoy Farm, Westonzoyland. Tealham Moor may have a small regular herd of up to 30. They leave from the first to the third week in March, rarely later, and there are records of odd stragglers through April, and even in the summer: one on Wet Moor, 18 July 1963, was apparently healthy, and two or three other birds, perhaps injured, have summered, together with one that had certainly escaped from Slimbridge. Away from the main wintering area, there have been a few records of single birds or small parties in flight over the south-west and at Minehead and Porlock Marshes.

Of five birds on Tealham Moor in December 1978 that had been colour-ringed at Slimbridge, the oldest was then ten.

North American race, the 'Tundra Swan' *C.c. columbianus*

Vagrant.

One, Hay Moor and Curry Moor, 5–24 January 1986, and on Curry Moor, 12 December 1987 into early 1988.

Whooper Swan *Cygnus cygnus*

Winter visitor; rare and erratic.

Before 1946, only two certain records, in 1805 and 1852, but some 'wild swans' on the levels may have been this species. There were five records from 1946 to 1955; from then till 1966, much more common, and a more or less regular winter visitor to the Parrett Estuary and the levels, including herds of up to 30. A total of at least 220 birds occurred in this period. Records then fell away again, and from 1967 to 1983 only about 64 were reported. Since then there have been only three records. Recent birds have been seen at many places on the levels, at Cheddar, Sutton Bingham, Durleigh and Ashford Reservoirs, and on one occasion flying over Bruton, but never in the west or south-west. Up to thirteen together; half the records in January and February, others November/December and March, with single reports in October and April.

We remain a little doubtful about the identity of some Whoopers reported between 1955 and 1966. Some claimed in more recent years have turned out to be Bewick's, and good telescopes were less common then than they are now.

Bean Goose   *Anser fabalis*

Winter visitor; very rare.

The first Somerset record was of two near Langport in December 1868. There were eight records from 1921 to 1963, involving a total of 12 birds. Since 1970, about 12 records of some 25 birds, often in association with swan herds on the levels, but also in Bridgwater Bay and at the major reservoirs; December to February, with one each October and November. Up to three have been seen together, and one flock of eight: Tealham and Tadham Moors, 23 February 1978. There were four records from Minehead and Porlock Marsh, 1947–63, but there have been none in the west since.

Pink-footed Goose   *Anser brachyrhynchus*

Vagrant.

The rarest grey goose in the county, with only 15 records since 1905 (seven since 1963). Recorded in all months from September to April, except November. Usually singly, but four parties of over ten have been noted, including a flock of 50 at Athelney, 11 April 1947; all on the levels, the coast of Bridgwater Bay, Cheddar Reservoir or the Dunster/Porlock shores.

White-fronted Goose *Anser albifrons*

Eurasian race *A.a. albifrons*
Winter visitor and passage-migrant; scarce and local.

Its numbers and distribution have always been sporadic, with small wintering parties wandering widely on the levels and the coast of Bridgwater Bay, the highest numbers usually appearing ahead of cold spells to the north or east. In the middle of this century it became for a time a more regular winter visitor: between 1950 and 1965 there was a main flock roosting in the Parrett Estuary which averaged 400 and occasionally rose to as much as 1000 or even 2000 (early 1963). These birds dispersed widely to feed over north and central Somerset, and south to Muchelney and West Sedge Moor. A smaller flock of between ten and 200 regularly visited Minehead Marshes from 1941 to 1967, with occasional larger numbers, such as 1000 seen on 4 February 1945.

However, since the mid-1960s there has been a decline. The Minehead flock disappeared just after the building of Butlin's Camp, which decreased the open area of the marshes, though occasional parties still appear there. The Parrett Estuary flock continued regular in small numbers of up to 150 till the early 1970s, then temporarily vanished, so that in 1974 only a single White-front was seen in the whole county. There has been some recovery recently, but numbers rarely exceed 60, although there were 400 in February

1979. These birds roost on Steart Island and feed mainly on Fenning Island and on the Pawlett Hams, visiting flooded levels when these are available.

Apart from these regular wintering birds, odd birds and small parties may appear almost anywhere on the coast and levels from December to early March, but especially during cold spells in January and February; rarely as early as 31 October or as late as April. There is probably some passage in late February and March. The one or two summer records may be of injured or escaped birds. There are no recent records from the east or the extreme south-west, and only one from Wimbleball Reservoir.

Greenland race *A.a. flavirostris*
Vagrant; not recently recorded.

About six records. One shot, River Parrett, 14 January 1951, had been ringed as a nestling at Umanak in Greenland, 29 July 1947.

Three, Steart, 28 December 1952, and one, Minehead Marshes, on the same date; two at Steart on 17 January 1953 were probably the same birds; two, Steart, 17 March 1956; single birds shot at Combwich, 24 December 1963 and 5 January 1964.

Greylag Goose Anser anser

Irregular visitor, now perhaps established as a semi-wild breeder; very local.

Earlier records, from 1920 to 1965, were probably of wild birds. Some 34 occurred in this period, mostly in coastal areas or on the levels from February to April. One at Steart, 8 April 1952, resembled the Eastern form *A.a. rubirostris*, but pink-billed birds also occur in western populations.

In the past 20 years, feral populations have become established in various places in southern England, and from about 1982 a small flock built up, based on Chilton Moor; they have bred here and on Westhay Heath. A pair tried to breed at Huntworth in 1986. We cannot know whether the birds seen outside this area are genuine wild stock from Scandinavia or Eastern Europe, or wandering British breeders. Since 1968 there have been 30 to 40 records which might refer to wild birds. If we reject all those which concern tame or summering geese, a total of about 160 birds remains, mostly from Cheddar Reservoir, around Bridgwater Bay or on the South Levels, with other records around Vobster and Mells, on the North Levels, at Durleigh and Sutton Bingham Reservoirs, near Taunton and at Minehead and Porlock Marshes; many of these were probably of British origin. Recorded in all months from September to April, but mostly from January to March; singly or in family parties, but four records of skeins of ten or more, the largest being 24 at Steart, 23 April 1974.

Canada Goose *Branta canadensis*

Resident; local. Winter visitor and passage-migrant; irregular.

Until well into this century it was not generally considered to be a wild bird, but we know that pairs had bred on several park lakes in the south-west before 1870, and a pair bred on Wells Moat in 1901. Wandering parties were occasional up to 1918, mostly in hard winters, but very few records were published up to the late 1950s; these were of small parties, mostly in spring, perhaps prospecting nest-sites.

In 1969 a pair reared five young at Clatworthy Reservoir, and these were apparently the originators of what is now the largest concentration in Somerset, amounting to a total of about 280 birds. They breed, not always successfully, at Clatworthy and in Butlin's Camp at Minehead, and since 1979 at Wimbleball Reservoir. It is not clear if the original stock came from birds introduced onto the Butlin's ponds or if they were wandering from established colonies outside Somerset: for example, Bicton in east Devon. The main flock is now fragmented, but it may sometimes be seen together on Minehead Marshes or while commuting between the Brendon Hill reservoirs and the coast. These birds are reinforced by small breeding stocks on newly created ponds in the same general area, at Torweston, Sandhill Farm, Billbrook, Sticklepath and elsewhere. They may be accompanied by odd wild geese or by exotics (especially Barnacle Geese) which may also have originated locally. The flock sometimes contains one or two birds of the smallest race, the Cackling Goose, *B.c. minima*.

In the last 15 years, pairs have also bred at several places to the south and east of the Brendon Hills – Fitzhead, Waterrow, and Drake's Lake at Wellington – and these have perhaps contributed to the main flock. Other pairs have bred at Orchardleigh Lake, Chilton Trinity Pits, Durleigh and Sutton Bingham Reservoirs, Enmore Park, East Quantoxhead, Witcombe

Bottom, Staplegrove and Taunton, and at least eight sites on ponds from Yeovil west to the Blackdowns.

From 1980 onwards, late-summer and autumn gatherings increased at Durleigh and Sutton Bingham, and these have in effect become wintering flocks, with up to 140 on each reservoir in late autumn, and rather fewer through the winter; in 1986 the Durleigh flock reached 200 in early October, and in 1987 reached the county record of 336 in September.

There are probably other unrecorded pairs on small waters, and an annual scatter of records of wandering parties throughout the county at all seasons, but especially in spring. One of the first pair to breed at Sutton Bingham had been ringed in its first year at the Bicton colony. Birds of the Sherborne Lake colony in Dorset have recently taken to visiting the extreme south-east of the county.

Barnacle Goose   *Branta leucopsis*

Winter visitor; very rare.

First recorded in 1809. One Victorian record and seven between 1917 and 1964. From about 1960, we cannot be sure whether birds seen were genuinely wild or had escaped from collections at Slimbridge or elsewhere. There have been about 14 occurrences since then of birds that could have been wild by their behaviour or by the place and time of the record. These have all been from mid-October to mid-March (most in January); mainly in the Parrett Estuary, with others accompanying swans on the South Levels, and at Tealham Moor, Cheddar Reservoir and Porlock Marsh. There is one extraordinary record of a flock that was certainly wild: on 17 March 1984, 78 appeared at Berrow and in the Parrett Estuary, declining to 20 by the 25th; one of these bore a green Dutch ring of a type put on birds of the Novaya Zemlya population that winter in Holland; this was the largest flock of these ever recorded in Britain.

Feral birds have recently occurred on many waters, and up to five have accompanied the Canada Goose flock in west Somerset.

Brent Goose *Branta bernicla*

Dark-bellied race *B.b. bernicla*
Winter visitor; scarce and local.

There is little information to show its status in the nineteenth century and there were only one or two records from 1900 to 1922; more regular from then to 1966, and annual since 1968.

About 70 per cent of all records come from the Parrett Estuary, where small numbers have been fairly regular in recent years from November to February; once September, occasionally October and March/April, and once May. Usually fewer than ten, exceptionally up to 36 (March 1979). Others have occurred since 1969 at the Axe Estuary, at Cheddar, Sutton Bingham and Wimbleball Reservoirs, at Dunster Beach, and in flight over Holcombe, Tonedale and Wellington. These have been mostly single birds or small parties, but two recent records of ten and 24 birds together at Dunster Beach, and one of 27 at Doniford. There were earlier records from flooded levels, 1879–1939, and one of two at North Petherton, 12 January 1962. Probably most frequent in hard winters; the recent increase reflects a series of good breeding seasons in the high Arctic and subsequent general increase in wintering birds.

Pale-bellied race *B.b. hrota*
Vagrant.

There were nine records from 1953 to 1986 of this Greenland and Canadian form, involving a total of 13 birds. Ten were at Steart, the others at the Axe Estuary, and at Minehead and Porlock Marsh; November to February, with three birds in late April. In 1987, a flock of 13 were seen at Steart, 12 October, and up to eight in December.

Egyptian Goose *Alopochen aegyptiacus*

Introduced. Has recently bred.

There were a number of Victorian records of escapes on the levels, and birds were kept before 1869 at Lydeard House and Cothelstone Pond. A pair bred in captivity at Spring Grove, Milverton, in 1915.

One was seen at Combwich, mid-summer 1979. A pair frequented Clatworthy and Wimbleball Reservoirs, 1980/81, and in 1982 bred successfully in an old Buzzard's nest at Wimbleball, rearing four young; they may have bred again in 1983 and certainly did so in 1986. A pair with three young were seen in Vivary Park, Taunton, in May 1986. In 1987, a pair was recorded around Bridgwater and a single bird near Creech St Michael.

Ruddy Shelduck   *Tadorna ferruginea*

Vagrant?

There have been at least eight records: two, Porlock Marsh, 13 November 1915, and one there, 12 May 1928; one, Durleigh Reservoir, 13 February 1977; male, Brean, 28 March 1978; two, Edithmead, 24 April and 1 May 1978; immature, Berrow, 4–10 June 1978; one, Parrett Estuary, May to September 1979; one, Sutton Bingham Reservoir, 16 March 1986.

It is possible that none of these were wild, although the first two were thought to be acceptable at the time. It has recently been concluded that there are no grounds for presuming that any British records in the past 50 years has definitely related to a wild vagrant (Rogers, 1982).

Shelduck   *Tadorna tadorna*

Resident, summer and autumn visitor and passage-migrant; locally common.

BES.

It has declined as a breeding bird, doubtless because of increasing disturbance in coastal areas inland from the Parrett Estuary, one of its previous strongholds. None now breed in the dunes from Brean to Berrow, recently heavily encroached on by holiday development, although odd pairs probably breed in most years inland to Brent Knoll. Breeding regularly recorded elsewhere in the Parrett Estuary, at Durleigh Reservoir and Porlock Marsh. It also breeds in the landslips of the western coast, and occasionally at other sites. No large creches have been recorded in recent years, when broods of up to 20 have been the norm.

Bridgwater Bay has long been known as one of a few important moulting grounds for this species, and this aspect has been extensively studied, in particular by Morley (1966, 1970, 1986). Those in June and July are usually transient birds en route to Continental moulting grounds, while those from late July to October are moulting birds. Counts vary considerably, but there is some evidence of a reduction, with recent counts rarely exceeding 2000.

Most birds winter on the coast between Brean Down and Hinkley Point, with highest numbers in the Parrett Estuary, where there is much movement between favoured sites. Typical coastal counts are of up to 500.

Inland, occurs on floods in small numbers, usually less than ten, rarely as many as 50. On the reservoirs, most frequent in spring and autumn; usually singly or in pairs, occasionally more.

Wood Duck *Aix sponsa*

This species remains in category 'D' of the British List, first reported in the early 1970s. About seven records, including several of pairs around Frome, are probably from the free-flying flock at Rode Bird Gardens. Twice at Durleigh Reservoir; a pair in Taunton, 15 April 1985, may have come from the nearby Virary Park collection.

Mandarin *Aix galericulata*

Visitor, mostly in autumn; rare.

Although this duck is now established as a breeding species in south-east England, the origin of Somerset birds is not clear. Most have been seen at Sutton Bingham Reservoir, where it has been annual since 1981. Up to four were present, 8 August–22 October 1982. Other records are generally of single birds or pairs. Modest attempts at introduction by the Wildfowl Trust in 1985/86 resulted in some releases at Somerton, and it remains to be seen how successful these are.

Wigeon   *Anas penelope*

Winter visitor and passage-migrant; locally common.

Birds usually arrive from the end of August, and numbers increase slowly to a peak from December to February. Numbers rapidly decline in March, and most have left by April. Occasional summer records may be of tame or injured birds.

Numbers vary considerably from year to year in response to the severity of the weather and flooding on the levels. The winter of 1981/82 was exceptional, with at least 32,000 in the county in January; most of these were on Southlake Moor, where an estimated 22,000 were there, on the 22nd. In milder years, with a lack of flooding at traditional sites such as Wet Moor, Curry Moor, King's Sedge Moor and West Sedge Moor, numbers may not exceed 1000.

Largest concentrations generally tend to be on the Central Levels, although in freezing conditions there is much movement within the county, particularly from inland areas to the coast. At such times, numbers in the Parrett Estuary may exceed 6000.

Wimbleball Reservoir holds the highest numbers in the west of the county, sometimes more than 500. There is some movement between here and Dunster Beach, most obvious in severe weather.

In the east, there is little suitable habitat and Wigeon are rarely recorded; five at Orchardleigh, 2 November 1980, were considered noteworthy.

American Wigeon   *Anas americana*

Vagrant.

About six records, all of adult males (females and immatures may well be overlooked): Cheddar Reservoir, 2–17 March 1946, and perhaps the same bird, 30 December 1946–26 January 1947; one at Shapwick, 5 April 1951, may have been an escape; Durleigh Reservoir, 23 February 1971; Sutton Bingham Reservoir, 24 March 1971; Cheddar Reservoir, 13 October 1976–21 February 1977; Wimbleball Reservoir, 30 January–20 March 1987 (what was presumed to be the same bird returned in the winter of 1987/8, see Appendix).

Gadwall   <small>*Anas strepera*</small>

Resident; scarce. Passage-migrant, summer and winter visitor; local.

It has undoubtedly increased in the county, as it has nationally, but is still far from common. Breeding had long been suspected before definite proof was obtained: a pair were observed mating at Sutton Bingham Reservoir, 18 May 1978, and in 1981 a pair bred successfully at Durleigh Reservoir, a female and five young being seen on 15 June. This was the first breeding record for the new county. Breeding again took place at Durleigh in 1983. In 1985, up to five pairs remained on Westhay Moor into June, and two juveniles at Cheddar Reservoir, 7 July, may have been reared locally. A female with two juveniles was seen on Westhay Moor in 1986.

A widespread, but never abundant passage-migrant, with records in every month. The highest numbers occur from late August to November on the major reservoirs, particularly Cheddar, where numbers may reach 200. In contrast, counts elsewhere rarely exceed 20, and 45 at Sutton Bingham Reservoir, 23 December 1982, were exceptional.

Not often seen on the coast, but does occur in winter in the Parrett Estuary, and sometimes at Dunster Beach.

Teal   <small>*Anas crecca*</small>

Nominate race *A.c. crecca*
Resident; rare. Passage-migrant and winter visitor; locally common.

Breeds annually in very small numbers on the peat-moors, and occasionally elsewhere on the levels.

Autumn and winter records at the reservoirs are very variable, often in hundreds, but sometimes more than 1000. Similar numbers may occur on flooded levels; in the winter of 1981/82, up to 4800 were on the South Levels.

Up to 1000 may occur in the Parrett Estuary from November to February, with smaller numbers elsewhere on the coast.

Green-winged Teal *A.c. carolinensis*
Vagrant

Six or seven records of this North American race, all of adult males: Porlock Marsh, 4 October 1951; Steart Point, 13 March 1965; Cheddar Reservoir, 17 January 1979; Durleigh Reservoir, 18 February 1979; Sutton Bingham Reservoir, 20 January 1980, 15 January and 6 February 1983.

Mallard *Anas platyrhynchos*

Resident, passage-migrant and winter visitor; locally common.

Despite anxiety about predation by Mink at some sites, it appears to be holding its own. Inadequate reports make numbers difficult to assess, but probably breeds in all 10-km squares within the county. The survey on the levels in 1983 found 404 males, 25 per cent of them on King's Sedge Moor. Breeding populations elsewhere, particularly in suburban areas, are often semi-domesticated; in some places, especially on the larger ponds in the east, they are reared for shooting.

Widespread, and sometimes abundant, both on passage and in winter. The main arrival is from mid-August, building up steadily in September and October, with counts of up to 500, rarely 1000. Most occur at the reservoirs or on the coast, and inland on floods.

Pintail *Anas acuta*

Passage-migrant and winter visitor; uncommon. Has bred.

Regular visitor to the coast and inland waters, reservoirs and levels, in variable numbers.

Generally arrives from mid-September, with most from December to February. The largest gatherings occur on the Central and South Levels, and

at Durleigh and Sutton Bingham Reservoirs. During the 1960s and 1970s, counts both here and in Bridgwater Bay often exceeded 100, and occasionally rose to 150. In 1980, there were 112 at Durleigh Reservoir in February, and 177 on the levels in the same period; however, in recent years, counts of more than 50 have been unusual.

Most depart by March, with very few recorded in spring in recent decades. Bred near Muchelney in 1951 and 1952.

Garganey   *Anas querquedula*

Passage-migrant; scarce. Has bred.

Recorded annually in small numbers, though in some years it is very scarce. Spring arrival is usually from mid-March, twice in February, with the earliest a pair at Huntworth, 25 February 1967. Most records are in single figures, usually individual males or pairs. However, in 1972, up to 20 occurred on Wet Moor and King's Moor, with 13 males there on 31 March; 15 on Curry Moor, 10 March 1974, was also exceptional.   Odd pairs sometimes remain in suitable breeding habitat until July, and breeding has on occasion been proved, most recently in 1979, when a pair raised three young on Tealham Moor.

Autumn passage is noted from mid-August, sometimes earlier, with Cheddar Reservoir the most regular site. Numbers rarely exceed five, but birds often remain for long periods, occasionally into early October.

Blue-winged Teal   *Anas discors*

Vagrant.

Two records: male, Porlock Marsh, 17 April 1981; female, Sutton Bingham Reservoir, 13 January 1982.

Shoveler   *Anas clypeata*

Passage-migrant and winter visitor; local. Has bred.

It may have bred more widely in the past, but the only recent proved records are on Chilton Moor and Catcott Heath in 1980.

It has been recorded in all months, the largest numbers from mid- to late winter. Most occur on the levels and at the reservoirs, with a scattering at other waters throughout the county. Small numbers winter on the coast, particularly in the Parrett Estuary, and irregularly at Dunster Beach and Porlock Marsh, where counts rarely exceed ten.

It has certainly declined in the last ten years, perhaps most noticeably on the South Levels and at Sutton Bingham Reservoir. In the 1970s, up to 500 in the King's Moor/Wet Moor area were not unusual, and over 200 regularly wintered at Sutton Bingham. However, by 1985, the highest counts in December were of 13 on West Sedge Moor and only 21 on the reservoir. The lack of flooding on the levels is an obvious reason for decline, although at Sutton Bingham this may be due to ecological changes; for notes on this see Introduction (p. 4).

Red-crested Pochard   *Netta rufina*

Occasional visitor.

This attractive duck is a popular collection bird, and is kept at various sites within the county. Breeding stock from the Bishop's Palace Moat at Wells are known to visit Cheddar Reservoir, where it has been regularly noted in autumn. Most used to be seen from October onwards, but in recent years has often occurred in early August. Some birds are obvious escapes, and although it is possible that others may be wild birds, many observers believe that few, if any, records are of genuine origin.

A drake in the Brue Estuary, 8 November 1984, was most unusual, as it is a bird rarely associated with the coast.

Pochard   *Aythya ferina*

Winter visitor and passage-migrant; locally common. Resident or summer visitor; local and rare.

One or two pairs breed in most years in the south of the county, and occasionally elsewhere.

Although birds are sometimes seen in the summer, the main arrival is from August, with highest numbers in November and December. Cheddar Reservoir usually holds the largest concentrations, although numbers vary considerably from year to year; there are usually around 500, but sometimes higher numbers, even up to 1000 or more. Recent counts here in September have shown over 80 per cent to be drakes, reflecting the different timing of migration between the sexes. Other reservoirs occasionally attract high numbers, as do flooded levels. Hawkridge Reservoir held 230 in November 1974, and Durleigh at least 1000 in February 1982, but these counts were exceptional.

Wintering parties are widely scattered, often on small brick-pits, ponds and similar waters, though numbers rarely exceed 30.

Up to ten regularly winter in the Parrett Estuary, but numbers here may be enhanced by hard weather, as in January 1985, when over 20 were seen.

Ring-necked Duck   *Aythya collaris*

Vagrant.

Most have been adult males in late autumn and winter. However, female and first-autumn birds may have been overlooked in the past because of identification difficulties.

The first record of this North American species was a long-staying male which frequented Cheddar Reservoir, as well as adjacent Avon reservoirs, on various dates from 1970 to 1973.

In April 1977, a drake with Pochard at Witcombe Bottom was also seen at nearby Sutton Bingham Reservoir. From 1979 to 1982 there were males at Cheddar and Hawkridge and Sutton Bingham Reservoirs, and at Witcombe Bottom. Two immature drakes were at Orchardleigh Lake, 22 November1980–17 January 1981.

One record of a female, Cheddar Reservoir, 26 August–13 October 1980.

Ferruginous Duck   *Aythya nyroca*

Vagrant.

Various *Aythya* hybrids and suspected escapes make assessment difficult, but this duck does undoubtedly occur as a genuine, if irregular, visitor.

The first record was of a bird shot at Lympsham, 14 February 1929, followed by a male at Durleigh Reservoir, 1 September 1945. Some subsequent records at Durleigh in the early 1950s were considered by Palmer and Ballance to be doubtfully identified. Two at Hawkridge Reservoir during March 1974 were published as possible escapes. Of the remainder, perhaps ten or so are considered acceptable; most have been of single birds, in every month except June–August.

Most records are from the major reservoirs, although there is one of a male in the Brue Estuary, April/May 1978.

Tufted Duck   *Aythya fuligula*

Resident, winter visitor and passage-migrant; local.

Although not a common breeding bird, there is some evidence of its expansion in recent years. It has bred, probably annually, at Hawkridge Reservoir since 1963, and does so regularly at Orchardleigh Lake, and at Durleigh and Sutton Bingham Reservoirs. Bred for the first time on Westhay Moor in 1985, and may have done so two years earlier. In 1986, five broods were reported from introduced birds at the Bishop's Palace Moat, Wells, and at least 15 pairs summered elsewhere in the county.

The small, but widespread, resident population is augmented from August

by passage birds and winter visitors, and quite small waters are used, as well as the principal reservoirs. Typical counts at Cheddar Reservoir, which holds the largest wintering population, range from 150 to 300, but numbers can rise to 700 or more in January, in response to freezing elsewhere. Elsewhere, high counts of 270, Durleigh Reservoir, December 1975, and 340 at Sutton Bingham Reservoir in December 1976; however, counts in the 1980s here have more typically been lower than 100. Numbers at Hawkridge are very variable, sometimes less than 10, but in some winters, such as 1986, as many as 80 have occurred. Departure and passage from late February to April, with a few remaining into May.

Very occasional on the coast, and only in small numbers.

Scaup *Aythya marila*

Winter visitor; scarce.

Large wintering flocks in the Bristol Channel are now a thing of the past; indeed, it is necessary to go back to 1930 to find any party in excess of 100. Nevertheless it is a regular, if uncommon, visitor, generally arriving from late September or October. Most have left by March, but some may linger as late as May in some years.   Many records are of single birds, although up to eleven have been seen at Cheddar Reservoir on occasion. Long stays of up to three months occur inland, but birds on the coast are usually seen briefly.

Hybridisation within the *Aythya* genus undoubtedly causes identification problems, particularly with females and immatures.

Eider   *Somateria mollissima*

Winter visitor; local and rare.

Formerly considered as a vagrant, but is now an annual visitor to the coast in small numbers, mainly in the winter. This increase probably reflects a national population expansion, and flocks regularly winter on the nearby South Wales coast.

Usually singly or in small parties, mostly off Brean Down and in the Parrett Estuary, and occasional elsewhere on the coast.

In 1972, a party of 20 off Sand Point (Avon) gradually dispersed, with ten to 13 remaining off Brean Down throughout the year.

Inland records are unusual anywhere, and eight at Cheddar Reservoir on 3 December 1978 were exceptional.

Long-tailed Duck   *Clangula hyemalis*

Winter visitor; rare.

Almost annual in recent years, from October to April, rarely to early May. Either singly or in twos; most of those aged and sexed with any certainty have been immature males.

Cheddar Reservoir is a particularly favoured site, and records here often refer to lengthy stayers. It has occurred at other major reservoirs, but a male on a drainage canal at North Newton for ten days in November/December 1974, and another on a small pond at Berrow, were exceptional. Rarely recorded on the coast, and in recent years, only three records of single birds: Brean Down, 23 January 1966; Parrett Estuary, 14 November 1983; and Stolford, 28 November 1987.

Common Scoter   *Melanitta nigra*

Passage-migrant and perhaps winter visitor; local and scarce.

It has been noted in every month, on all parts of the coast, though rarely in large parties, and typically less than 20. A flock of 60 flying north off Brean Down, 23 April 1977, was noteworthy. Most are in spring and autumn, and the larger reservoirs are regularly visited in July, when overland passage occurs. The largest count for Somerset is of 97 at Sutton Bingham Reservoir, 6 November 1982, which stayed briefly during a gale.

Velvet Scoter   *Melanitta fusca*

Winter visitor; rare.

Recorded annually 1984–7 and, although very uncommon, may be a more regular visitor than previously supposed.

The first coastal record was of two in the Parrett Estuary, 22 November 1958. At least ten since, all but one between Brean Down and Hinkley Point, the exception being a male off Dunster Beach, 21 December 1985.

There are five inland records: male, Durleigh Reservoir, 7–12 November 1949; male, Chard Reservoir, 12 February 1956; male, Durleigh Reservoir, 11 November 1962; male, Cheddar reservoir, 5 December 1972, and two immatures there on 22nd, which left in the direction of the coast.

Goldeneye   *Bucephala clangula*

Winter visitor and passage-migrant; locally common.

A regular and widespread winter visitor since the building of reservoirs. Arrival from mid-October, with highest counts from November to February. Departure from March, with some, mostly immatures, remaining till late April or rarely May; display is frequently observed during the spring.

Most of the major reservoirs have wintering populations, typically of 10–20; small numbers occur on floods, brick-pits and other waters, and occasionally on the coast.

Cheddar Reservoir regularly holds the highest numbers, and numbers have increased here during the 1980s: counts of more than 20 were unusual, but at least 100 have been regular since 1982.

Smew   *Mergus albellus*

Winter visitor; rare.

It has occurred throughout the county on the major reservoirs and on suitable areas of flooding, mainly from December to February.

Most frequently females or immatures, either singly or in twos. Scarce in some years, its arrival is normally dependent on harsh weather conditions: in 1979, up to four were at Cheddar Reservoir in January and February, and six at Sutton Bingham Reservoir, 24/25 February. An influx in 1985 during severe weather in the first two months of the year brought as many as 20 to the county, with up to four together on Westhay Moor, Tealham Moor and King's Sedge Moor.

Red-breasted Merganser   *Mergus serrator*

Winter visitor and passage-migrant; scarce.

This duck has never been common in Somerset, probably due to the unsuitable nature of the coast and estuaries. Most records are of single birds or small parties, but more than five is most unusual. Most occur between November and March, occasionally in other months, but a male on Shapwick Heath, 24–27 May 1982, was exceptional.

The majority are seen in flight on the coast, or for one or two days on inland waters. In some years there have been only single records and it is only in hard winters that birds stay for any length of time. In 1979, seven were at Cheddar Reservoir, 16 February, with four till 20 March, and one stayed at a Highbridge brick-pit from 22 February to 3 March; others were seen in the Axe Estuary, at Steart and at Durleigh.

Goosander *Mergus merganser*

Winter visitor and passage-migrant; scarce.

Most are seen from December to March, less often from October to April, but numbers tend to fluctuate in response to weather conditions. Infrequent on the coast, although odd birds appear most years, seen usually in flight in the Parrett Estuary and occasionally elsewhere. Most occur inland on the reservoirs, deeper floods and rhynes; up to ten have been seen as far inland as Orchardleigh Lake and Sutton Bingham Reservoir. The most regular site is now Wimbleball Reservoir, where up to 40 have been recorded.

In prolonged freezing conditions, there is an influx of birds from the Avon reservoirs, and up to 20 may use Cheddar Reservoir and the nearby rhynes of Tealham, Tadham and Westhay Moors. Harsh weather in 1979 brought a record 44 to Cheddar Reservoir on 8 January.

Ruddy Duck *Oxyura jamaicensis*

Irregular visitor in variable numbers.

Now well established at the Avon reservoirs of Blagdon and Chew Valley, where wintering numbers have grown dramatically. Although scarce, has been seen in most months at Cheddar Reservoir. Small numbers usually arrive in September/October, but it is in freezing conditions that most occur. The shallow margins at Chew Valley make it more prone to freezing, and in February 1979 many moved to Cheddar, where the record count of 206 occurred on the 25th. As conditions improve, birds are quick to leave for waters with more natural surroundings.

Only small numbers at other reservoirs, and very scarce on floods. Rare on the coast, but has occurred on at least three occasions in the Parrett Estuary.

DUCK COUNTS

The following counts are derived by taking the average of peak counts of eight regular species at four major reservoirs in the period 1982–6.

Cheddar Reservoir

	Jan	Feb	Mar	Apr	May	Jun	Jul	Aug	Sep	Oct	Nov	Dec
Wigeon	92	28	8	1				3	39	60	39	32
Gadwall	21	15	9	2		1	2	18	69	75	63	27
Teal	84	37	2	1			1	54	580	215	65	34
Mallard	266	199	52	12	22	46	75	295	492	670	384	393
Shoveler	81	102	51	5	1			9	48	96	33	63
Pochard	775	395	139	6				110	540	644	508	412
Tufted Duck	507	287	203	28			1	5	163	185	133	220
Goldeneye	64	69	37	13						8	38	77

Durleigh Reservoir

	Jan	Feb	Mar	Apr	May	Jun	Jul	Aug	Sep	Oct	Nov	Dec
Wigeon	221	333	293								2	26
Gadwall	13	11	2	2				2	5	1	1	3
Teal	582	159	42					4	9	33	158	448
Mallard	309	165	53	10	8	80	87	605	475	175	132	395
Shoveler	6	2	2	1				1	1	1	1	4
Pochard	287	217	139	3				2	2	11	38	83	115
Tufted Duck	58	35	23	14	1			1	14	10	10	16	20
Goldeneye	1	1	1							1	1	1

Wimbleball Reservoir

	Jan	Feb	Mar	Apr	May	Jun	Jul	Aug	Sep	Oct	Nov	Dec
Wigeon	270	176	50						4	3	54	94
Gadwall	2										1	1
Teal	73	34	24						12	28	62	65
Mallard	209	105	60	6	6			65	131	158	140	163
Shoveler		1										1
Pochard	22	30	8	2			1	1	5	7	39	41
Tufted Duck	30	36	29	17	5	2	2	2	15	18	31	28
Goldeneye	3	5	4							1	2	2

	Jan	Feb	Mar	Apr	May	Jun	Jul	Aug	Sep	Oct	Nov	Dec
Sutton Bingham Reservoir												
Wigeon	950	775	437	24				2	1	6	63	336
Gadwall	17	15	8	1	1	1	1	1	1	2	8	12
Teal	283	171	21	10		1	2	78	49	52	102	229
Mallard	258	235	64	38	45	73	146	233	389	247	257	180
Shoveler	27	26	9	4	1		1	8	11	13	14	22
Pochard	107	47	31	6	2	2	4	7	7	47	115	96
Tufted Duck	140	112	68	70	53	43	49	62	97	66	82	68
Goldeneye	6	7	8	6	1					2	2	3

Honey Buzzard   *Pernis apivorus*

Formerly a rare summer visitor and passage-migrant. Now vagrant.

Reported about seven times before 1890, and bred on the Quantocks in 1898 and 1899.

Only six records this century, all of single birds: three from Sutton Bingham Reservoir; single birds near Burton Pynsent Monument; Durleigh Reservoir; and Brean Down; all between 27 June and 23 October.

Black Kite   *Milvus migrans*

Vagrant.

The only accepted record is of one near Bruton, 18 May 1986.

Red Kite   *Milvus milvus*

Rare visitor and passage-migrant; formerly bred.

Bred before 1850, at least in the west. Only 16 or 17 recorded, 1850–1965. About 34 since, but some records are believed to have involved the same birds. Recorded in every month except August; the main periods are March–May (15 records involving about 13 birds), and September–November (11 birds). The recent increase in sightings reflects the increasing population in Wales due to vigorous protection. As Welsh juveniles are thought to disperse in a south-east direction a few weeks after fledging, this would appear to be the source from which most of our birds originate in the autumn. The spring birds are no doubt also part of the Welsh stock, returning to their natal area. If the breeding population continues to expand, we could hope that this fine bird will one day return to breed in the wooded hillsides of Somerset.

Has been widely reported, but most frequently from the coast and the hills in the west. Most birds are seen on one or two days only, but on occasions they will spend a few days or even weeks in an area. A bird reported from Exmoor during the summer of 1970 was eventually found poisoned on 29 March 1971; analysis by the RSPB showed heavy residues of strychnine.

White-tailed Eagle   *Haliaeetus albicilla*

Vagrant, but formerly a rare winter visitor.

At least 12 seen or shot between 1811 and 1912, mainly between Bridgwater and Minehead, where apparently they were almost regular, sometimes occurring in pairs. The only record outside this period is of an immature, which was shot at Steart, 1 December 1945.

Egyptian Vulture   *Neophron percnopterus*

Vagrant.

The only record is of an immature shot, Kilve Cliffs, in October 1825 or 1826.

Marsh Harrier *Circus aeruginosus*

Passage-migrant; rare but increasing. Has bred.

A pair bred, rearing two young, in 1986; the following year the male returned, joined briefly by a female early in the season, but unfortunately she did not stay. A male and up to four different females present in 1988.

Otherwise a rare passage-migrant. About 21 between 1924 and 1966, 10 in spring (15 March–23 May) and the remainder in the autumn and early winter (16 August–10 January, once in February).

Since then at least 50, mainly on the levels or in the Parrett Estuary. Apart from one January record (1977) all fall roughly into the two main migration periods. The majority are in the spring, with a smaller number from 15 August to 25 October. Most birds move through quickly but in 1986 a female and an immature were present in the Parrett Estuary from August to October.

Hen Harrier *Circus cyaneus*

Winter visitor and passage-migrant; scarce. Formerly bred.

Once bred fairly regularly on Exmoor, at least until 1910; breeding possibly occurred about 1920 and in 1925.

About 60 between 1920 and 1966 (33 since 1951). Few noted during the 1960s but since then there has been a gradual increase.

Apart from a few summer records, mainly a passage-migrant and winter visitor, in variable numbers. The main arrival in the autumn is during October and November (occasionally as early as August); usually leaves March/April (latest, 11 May). Mostly reported from the Central Levels, the coastal strip from Brean Down to the Parrett Estuary, and Exmoor (where there is a predominance of males). Occasionally a roost of up to three birds occurs at Berrow, usually after an influx from the Continent.

Montagu's Harrier   *Circus pygargus*

Formerly a rare passage-migrant and non-breeding summer visitor; now a vagrant. Has bred.

There were five breeding records between 1850 and 1920, all in the west of the county. Pairs were also present in at least four summers between 1927 and 1965.

Only eleven records since, all since 1971, mainly from the heaths and levels, between 16 April and 12 September. These include three records in 1988: a 'ring-tailed' bird with a Marsh Harrier at Stolford, 16 April, a male near Langport two days later, and another 'ring-tail' at Steart, 16 May.

Goshawk   *Accipiter gentilis*

Formerly a vagrant; now probably a rare resident.

The first county record was near Pinkworthy Pond on 15 September 1960, followed by one at Horner in 1962. Since then birds have been seen in 1967, 1971, and each subsequent year with the exceptions of 1972, 1973 and 1977. Most reports relate to single birds, but on occasions pairs are seen at suitable breeding localities, and display noted; although breeding is likely, it has yet to be proved.

Records are spread over most of the county, but few are seen on more than one or two dates at a locality; however, there are recent records of some remaining for several months.

Sparrowhawk   *Accipiter nisus*

Resident, passage-migrant and winter visitor; fairly common.

A fairly common resident in the more wooded areas, becoming more widespread outside the breeding season. Following persecution by game-keepers at the turn of the century, this species was greatly reduced by an accumulation of toxic chemicals between 1957 and 1960. It declined over the greater part of Britain during this period, becoming almost extinct as a breeding species in some parts. However, the Somerset population appears to have held its own.

The *Breeding Atlas* confirmed breeding in 21 of the county's 10-km squares, with possible or probable breeding in a further 8. Since then the population appears to have increased steadily to its present healthy level.

Occurs as a passage-migrant and winter visitor in small numbers, but such movement is difficult to detect among the resident birds. One ringed at Steart, 26 October 1985, was found dead in Jylland, Denmark, 12 October 1986.

Buzzard   *Buteo buteo*

Resident; locally common. Also passage-migrant and possible winter visitor.

The main distribution is to the south and west of a line drawn between the Parrett Estuary and Yeovil, by far the most favoured areas being the hill country of the Quantocks, the Blackdowns and Exmoor. Smaller numbers occur in the hills to the south with a few scattered pairs on the Mendips and the hill ridges around the levels.

More widespread outside the breeding season, with birds appearing more frequently on the levels and the coast. It is difficult to know if these are visitors from outside the county or wanderers from the surrounding hills. Occurs as a passage-migrant in small numbers, but these birds are more easily detected on the coast away from the breeding areas.

Probably common until the early nineteenth century, but was exterminated by 1850 from everywhere except Exmoor and perhaps part of the Quantocks. There was a steady increase from 1915 until the mid-1950s, but it was then severely hit by myxomatosis which affected its main prey, the rabbit. Probably recovered within 10 to 15 years and continues to do well; some areas, especially in the south and west, may well be holding maximum numbers.

With details from the *Breeding Atlas*, the BTO Buzzard survey in 1983, and additional records since, there is confirmed breeding in 29 of the county's 10-km squares with probable or possible breeding in a further 10. The breeding population in 1983 was thought to be more than 100 pairs.

SPECIFIC LIST 107

Rough-legged Buzzard *Buteo lagopus*

Vagrant.

About 18 records, mainly of single birds. Most have occurred between November and April, with odd records on the levels, but most in the west of the county. Although most are adequately described, some records may refer to light-plumaged Common Buzzards.

Osprey *Pandion haliaetus*

Formerly a vagrant, now a rare passage-migrant.

Seven recorded during the last century (1837–94), followed by five up to 1966 (two in spring, three in autumn).

Since then about 35 have been recorded from 15 localities throughout the county. Apart from three on the coast at Brean Down/Axe Estuary, they are mainly noted at the reservoirs, especially Sutton Bingham. Most records in autumn from August to November, latest on the 8th (1938), and 13 in spring between March and May, earliest 29th. Four in the summer (June/July) which includes what was considered a second-year bird at Sutton Bingham, noted on five dates between 5 May and 6 July 1978 – an unusually long stay.

Kestrel *Falco tinnunculus*

Resident, passage-migrant and probably winter visitor; fairly common.

A widespread and fairly common resident, and a passage-migrant in small numbers, usually April/May and September–November, especially on the coast, where such movements are more easily detected. Breeds throughout the county, but numbers appear to fluctuate, with low numbers reported 1978, 1979, 1985 and 1986, perhaps due to shortage of prey. Results from the *Breeding Atlas* confirmed breeding in 30 of the county's 10-km squares, with probable or possible breeding in a further five; it was surprisingly absent in four squares, but has since been proved to breed in at least one of these. Some dispersal probably occurs from the high ground during the winter.

Red-footed Falcon   *Falco vespertinus*

Vagrant.

Three records: male, Brean Down, 8 June 1969; immature male beside the M5 at Walrow (Highbridge), 22–24 May 1980; immature male, near Yoxter, 28 July–3 August 1985.

Merlin   *Falco columbarius*

Summer visitor; very local and rare. Winter visitor and passage-migrant; scarce.

It maintains a tenuous foothold as a breeding species on Exmoor; occasionally as many as five pairs nest, but more usually only one or two, and it has declined, as it has nationally. Easily disturbed not only by the general public but also by bird-watchers, and unfortunately still harassed by egg-collectors.

Occurs as a passage-migrant and winter visitor on the coast, reservoirs and levels; although movement often difficult to detect, three were noted flying north over Shapwick Heath, 1 April 1986. Arrives in August, occasionally earlier (16 July 1983), but the main arrival and passage is from September to November. Departure in March/April; a few records into May (latest, 22 May 1969). The early and late birds probably migrants, with the wintering birds not arriving until October and leaving by April.

Hobby   *Falco subbuteo*

Summer visitor and passage-migrant; local and rare.

This species can be rather elusive in the breeding-season, and many pairs probably go undetected. Breeding has taken place or been suspected at various times in many places, but not in coastal areas. In a typical year, about four pairs may breed. The *Breeding Atlas* confirmed breeding in seven of the county's 10-km squares, with probable or possible breeding in a further four, probably involving ten to fifteen pairs.

The earliest published sighting is on the early date of 18 February 1978 at Lilstock. However, they do not usually arrive until mid- or late April, with the main arrival in May. Most sightings occur between June and August, with fewer noted in July than the other two months; this may be due to the incubating birds not being visible. Leaves toward the end of August and during September, with occasional sightings into October, the latest on the 23rd.

Gyrfalcon   *Falco rusticolus*

Vagrant.

One of the Greenland race *F.r. candicans* was found disabled at Watchet on 20 February 1926, and died the following day.

Peregrine   *Falco peregrinus*

Resident; local and rare. Winter visitor and passage-migrant; scarce.

The well-documented national decline due to the use of organochlorine pesticides exterminated all Somerset's breeding pairs. Decreased from being a local breeding resident during the first half of the century to become extinct as a breeding species by about 1957. A voluntary ban on certain chemicals in 1962 and 1965, mainly aldrin and dieldrin, brought about a slight recovery, which began to be noticed in the early 1970s, with increasing numbers of passage and wintering birds. This increase has been maintained during the past decade.

The odd pair or two remained near suitable breeding sites, but it was not until 1980 that the Peregrine returned to breed. Up to five pairs have bred each year since, using six or seven sites, and at least 17 young are known to have fledged between 1980 and 1986.

As a passage-migrant and winter visitor it has been widely reported, with the exception of the east side of the county. The most favoured areas include the levels and the Parrett Estuary; at times up to six individuals may be present at both places during the winter.

Red Grouse *Lagopus lagopus*

Resident (introduced); very local and declining. Also vagrant.

A female was shot on Black Down, 24 September 1884. The only other record which suggests a genuine vagrant was a female found freshly dead at Greenaleigh Point, 27 March 1966.

Although Exmoor introductions were attempted in the last century, birds were not properly established until after 1916, on the Oare Manor estate. By

1939, they were well distributed on heather moorland; although reduced by wartime disturbance, they recovered well after 1945. By 1976 there were perhaps 40 pairs, mainly on the north-east part of the Moor, from Dunkery Hill north-west to Chetsford, with a few further west, as far as Brendon Common in Devon, and isolated pairs on Winsford Hill and Withypool Common. By 1978, they seem to have been reduced to some 12 pairs, and since then there have been no Somerset records away from the north-east, except for two near Pinkworthy Pond, 31 January 1982. Breeding has continued in very small numbers in the Dunkery Hill/Chetsford area, but the population may now be so small that extinction is inevitable. The main reason for the decline may well be disturbance.

From 1948 to 1977 there were about seven Quantock records, but we do not know whether introduction was ever attempted there. One was seen at Bicknoller Post, 25 June 1986. Stragglers used to occur on the Brendon Hills when the Exmoor population was higher, but there is now hardly any suitable country left there.

Black Grouse *Tetrao tetrix*

Formerly local resident; now extinct.

Until 1914, it was a fairly common bird on heather moorland and heathland, especially near birch woods, on the Quantocks, the Blackdowns, the Brendon Hills and Exmoor. It also occurred on the Mendips. The Acland game-books for Winsford and Holnicote show an average of 70 shot per season, 1836–1906, the record bag being 208 in 1896. There was no sign of a decrease at the end of this period.

After 1918 there was a rapid decline. Little is known of the Blackdown population, but probably few after 1920, the year which they last bred on the Mendips. On the Quantocks, remained common till the late 1940s, but then declined until thought extinct by 1968; there was then a strong recovery, with up to 12 seen together in 1974, yet the last birds were seen in December 1977. On Exmoor, became increasingly confined to the north-east. From 1968 to 1970, the National Park Committee tried to introduce Scottish birds, hand-reared at North Molton (Devon) and Holnicote. Some survived for a time in the wild, and at least one brood was hatched in the Kinsford Gate area, but the decline continued. The last breeding at Winsford Hill took place about 1970. The last lek on the Moor was in 1972, and the very last bird, a female, was seen on Lucott Moor at dusk on the day of the Prince of Wales's wedding, 29 July 1981.

Two records of vagrant males should be mentioned: Mendip, 19 September 1963; Langford Heathfield, 19 December 1968.

Probably the main cause of extinction was disturbance. It is hard for us to realise how empty the moors were before the motor-car. One Exmoor stronghold, the stunted pine plantations on Culbone Hill, was tidied up and partly destroyed in the 1960s and 1970s, and the last known leks were often near roads; a favourite grassy area on Wilmersham Common was far too vulnerable and may even have been too much visited by bird-watchers.

Red-legged Partridge   *Alectoris rufa*

Resident (introduced); local.

First introduced around Cheddar about 1817. From then till 1920, most regularly reported from the Mendips between there and Brean Down, especially Wavering Down and Crook Peak, where a wild population has remained till the present day. There were probably introductions in other places in the nineteenth and early twentieth centuries, but most records that we have are from the south-west. It remained very local up to the late 1970s. In that decade, introduced around Wembdon and Spaxton and found to be regular in the Norton St Philip/Orchardleigh area; also frequently reported from Steart, around Somerton and Curry Rivel, on the South Levels and at South Petherton; west of the Quantocks only at Cothelstone and Porlock Marsh. There were a few records from a number of places in the north, south and south-west.

Since 1980, it has been much more common, because of widespread introductions, for example at Norton St Philip, Pawlett, Cricket St Thomas, Wembdon and Bridgetown; by 1986, occurring as far west as Simonsbath. It will be interesting to see if it can sustain itself in the wild away from places of introduction.

Both species of partridge may well be under-recorded, since large areas of agricultural land are seldom visited by bird-watchers. It has yet to be established whether any Chukar strains have been introduced.

Grey Partridge   *Perdix perdix*

Resident; local and scarce.

Distribution and numbers hard to assess. It is partly supported by local introductions, and may go unobserved for years.

Partridges were obviously far more common in the nineteenth and early twentieth centuries than they are today. A bag of 1086 in two days at Stogursey in October 1897 is now inconceivable, and in fact little Partridge shooting takes place in some years. Most observers dated the serious decline from about 1970, though it had probably begun well before that. In 1966, birds were reported from 27 places, the same number as 1982; these had risen to 38 in 1975. The mid-1980s have shown better results (or perhaps merely better coverage?) with 48 places listed in 1985; rather fewer in 1986. Breeding has often suffered from wet summers, but no doubt the main cause of decline have been the destruction of field-side cover and the use of toxic sprays. We know little of the extent of most introductions, which are better documented for the other species.

About 70 per cent of all recent records have been below the 10-m contour, on the levels and in the coastal areas. Apparently very scarce in the north-east and the east, and on the Mendips. Extremely local or absent in the hills of the south and in the south-west. Rare in the west: beyond the Quantocks, recently recorded from West Bagborough, Bicknoller, Watchet, Timberscombe, the Porlock Vale and the Brendon Hills, with one strange record from Kinsford Gate. Some of these are the result of introductions.

Quail   *Coturnix coturnix*

Summer visitor and passage-migrant; rare and irregular.

Quail have never been more than irregular breeders, at least in modern times. In the nineteenth century, breeding was proved in the Bridgwater and Taunton areas, and at Badgworth, King's Sedge Moor and Seavington St Mary, and from 1900 to 1965 on the Central and South Levels, in the north-east Quantocks, on the Brendon Hills and in the Porlock Vale.

Since then, there have been records in 18 summers, by far the best season being 1970, when 22 places were involved. Breeding was proved near Culbone in 1966, in the Brendon Hills in 1976, at West Bagborough in 1983; it probably took place at Luccombe in 1980. But birds must have bred in other years, and many go unrecorded. About half of all Quail have been heard or seen on the levels, especially on Somerton Moor and West Sedge Moor; another quarter come from the Brendon Hills and the south-west; others from the Mendips, the South Levels and the coastal area west of Watchet; and there are a few other records from elsewhere, though not from the south-east.

Most birds are heard from June to August, less commonly from mid-May.

There have recently been two April records, the earlier being an extra-ordinary one of a bird calling at 01.30 at Holnicote, 7 April 1980. In recent years, not reported after 8 September, but there are earlier records up to December, and even two for January.

Pheasant   *Phasianus colchicus*

Resident; locally common.

Common throughout Somerset on lower ground with adequate cover, but not abundant unless preserved. Numbers are augmented every year by introductions, often in thousands of birds, especially in the south. There are few on higher ground in the west, and they are normally absent from Exmoor valleys. There are, however, records of wanderers on open moorland, here and on the Quantocks, and even of one oiled beach casualty.

Golden Pheasant   *Chrysolophus pictus*

Recently introduced.

Introduced around Orchardleigh in 1973, several remaining till 1977. One at Park End, Quantocks, 22 October 1978, was perhaps a wanderer from further afield.

Water Rail   *Rallus aquaticus*

Resident; very scarce and local. Winter visitor and passage-migrant; local.

Breeding has always been hard to prove. The few certain records have been:

Meare	1900 and 1902
Mells Park	1920
South Levels	1956
Shapwick Heath	1957

Queen's Sedge Moor	1969
Westhay Heath	1983–88 – at least two pairs
Stogumber	1985
Vobster	1986

It has probably bred fairly regularly on the peat-moors in recent years, and also at Huntworth and on Berrow Marsh. There are summer records since 1970 from the Brue Estuary, the South Levels and Porlock Marsh, and May reports from Charterhouse and Priddy Pools.

A widespread passage-migrant and winter visitor in marshy places throughout the county. Mostly September to March, with a few in August and April; the majority from November to February. There have been between 55 and 70 records every season since 1979, except for 1982/83, when there were only 38. Most of these were from the levels, especially the peat-moors, or at Berrow Marsh and Dunster Hawen, and they include counts of up to ten together in small areas of the levels.

Spotted Crake *Porzana porzana*

Vagrant, or rare winter visitor and passage-migrant. Has bred.

Apparently a fairly common resident on the levels in the mid-nineteenth century, though not proved to breed till 1930, when two nests were found near Burtle, two on 'Sedge Moor' and perhaps one near Muchelney; another was found at Catcott Heath in 1933.

From 1857 to 1936, about 18 detailed records, mostly from the North and Central Levels; dates range from August to February.

Eleven records from 1958 to 1976; with the exception of two on West Moor, 23 July 1964, and two at Dunwear Pit, 12 January 1974, the rest have been single birds, 7 August–9 December. Three records on Porlock Marsh, two at Screech Owl, Huntworth, and singles at Berrow Marsh, and Sutton Bingham Reservoir.

One recent record: one, Durleigh Reservoir, 23 September 1986.

Little Crake *Porzana parva*

Vagrant.

One record: a bird shot at Bridgwater before 1867.

Baillon's Crake *Porzana pusilla*

Vagrant.

Five old records: near Taunton, early October 1870 and 29 September 1874; Stogursey, 1887; Axbridge, September 1901; Minehead, 12 or 13 November 1912.

Corncrake *Crex crex*

Now vagrant, or very rare passage-migrant. Formerly bred.

In the mid-nineteenth century, a common summer visitor to farmland and to the levels. A slow decrease began about 1870, and by 1900 it was already scarce except on the levels. This decline continued, till by 1925 it was already absent from large areas, though remaining fairly common on unreclaimed levels and in parts of central and west Somerset. The last definite breeding record was on the South Levels in 1954, but a few probably bred elsewhere until the mid-1950s, and one pair at Bicknoller as late as 1964. Breeding may have occurred at West Quantoxhead in 1970 and on West Sedge Moor in 1972. From 1965 to 1986, about 25 were recorded in various places, West Sedge Moor in particular; late April to early September, especially May, and one was found dead at Porlock in October 1982.

Birds used to arrive and pass through in late April and early May. Breeders left and there was a marked passage, as appears from game-books, from late August to early October; two records in December and one in February.

Moorhen   *Gallinula chloropus*

Resident, passage-migrant and winter visitor; locally common.

A common resident in most damp places on the lower ground, wherever enough cover is available for breeding. Birds tend to concentrate on larger waters in autumn and winter, where they are joined by immigrants from northern Europe: one ringed in Denmark in August 1951 was recovered on Curry Moor in December 1954. Some birds probably pass at both seasons.

The highest concentrations are on the levels, and Moorhens are everywhere scarce or absent on higher ground, though they do occur in summer wherever there is still water and shelter. Generally rare or absent on Exmoor, even in the valleys.

There was evidently some decrease in the 1970s, perhaps due to the removal of cover on the levels and to the predation by Mink. Few series of counts are available, but such evidence as we have shows high numbers in the 1960s: thus, counts of 84, at Chard Reservoir, 12 December 1968, and of 200, Bridgwater, 27 October 1967, have not been approached since then. But there may have been some recovery very recently: there were 27 families on Westhay Moor and Heath in 1983, though the 83 pairs found by the RSPB Levels Survey in the same year seems on the low side by former standards. On the other hand, a single observer found 65 breeding pairs on the North Levels in 1985. In good seasons nesting may be prolonged into September. Birds have often been seen gathering to feed on fallen fruit in early autumn.

Coot   *Fulica atra*

Resident, winter visitor and passage-migrant; locally common.

A resident on most waters over about 0.3ha, and occasionally on smaller ponds; scarce in the west and parts of the south-west. Not known to breed

between the Quantocks and the Devon border, except at Wimbleball
Reservoir, Dunster Hawen, and Butlin's Camp, Minehead. There is an
autumn concentration, reinforced by immigrants, on the major reservoirs –
Cheddar, Durleigh, Sutton Bingham, and recently Wimbleball – which
normally hold between them a wintering population of between 2500 and
4500; of these, at least 75 per cent are at Cheddar, which holds the record
count for any Somerset water: 5000, 28 December 1963. In the past, Coot
were widespread on winter flooding, and they can still be found there when it
occurs, for instance on Southlake Moor.

Autumn numbers build up from July to October or November; they then
decline slightly for the winter and fall off steeply in March. In hard winters,
birds appear on coasts and rivers.

A recent development has been the colonisation of peat-moors. Suitable
breeding pits are sometimes pumped out too early for birds to succeed in
breeding, but at least 17 families were reared on Westhay Moor in 1986.

Crane   *Grus grus*

Vagrant.

Three old records of single birds before 1889. In 1963 there was a
late-autumn influx into southern England, and parties were noted in a
number of places: up to 48, Sutton Bingham Reservoir, 29 October; 39 over
Stogursey, with others heard over Stolford, on the 30th; 13, near the
Huntspill River, and seven over Ilminster, on the 31st.

The only recent record is of one flying over Bridgwater, 22 April 1986.

Little Bustard   *Tetrax tetrax*

Vagrant.

Three records of single birds: 'Sedge Moor', about 1872; an immature female
shot near Drayton, 19 October 1894, assigned then to the 'western race',
although the species is now regarded as monotypic; Isle Abbotts, 28
December 1914.

Great Bustard Otis tarda

Vagrant.

One record: a bird seen from a train on Shapwick Heath, 27 September 1870. A rare example of a Victorian sight-record being generally accepted, the observer being the well-known ornithologist J.E. Harting, and the train unlikely to have been an express!

Oystercatcher Haematopus ostralegus

Resident, passage-migrant, winter visitor and non-breeding summer visitor; locally fairly common.

Formerly a more common breeder, with up to 16 pairs on Steart Island in 1960, reduced to only one pair in 1986. Bred formerly at Berrow, but there is now too much disturbance. Has bred at Steart Point since at least the 1930s: one to three nests, and now most regular in the scrapes, where one or two pairs breed in most years; occasionally at Wall Common, Stolford and West Huntspill. Few other suitable sites in the county.

Most birds occur in the Parrett Estuary and on the coast from Steart to Stolford, with small numbers at Minehead and Porlock. Wintering birds are mainly of Faeroese, Icelandic and Scottish origin. Adults leave the estuaries in February and March and are replaced by migrants from further south; average April counts of 140 in the Parrett Estuary.

Summering non-breeding birds in July are joined by the early passage birds, with highest counts in August and September, decreasing steadily, October to December. Perhaps more numerous in recent years, with up to 460 in the Parrett Estuary; exceptionally 630, in September 1986. Up to 150 from Blue Anchor to Minehead and at Porlock, although 280 have been recorded.

Scarce away from the coast. Mostly at Cheddar, Sutton Bingham and Durleigh Reservoirs; one record from Chard Reservoir, and occasionally on the levels and elsewhere on passage. Small movement in March and again in May; then passage from mid-July to mid-September, mostly in early August. Usually ones and twos, but exceptional records have been: 18 over Wellington, 16 October 1976; 25 flying west at Cheddar, 3 January 1984, and 37 south, 6 August 1977.

Black-winged Stilt *Himantopus himantopus*

Vagrant.

Six records of single birds: near Bridgwater (probably Chilton Moor), before 1858; Polsham, 1 July 1896; Cheddar Reservoir, 4 September 1938; Porlock Marsh, 23 July–4 August 1960; Steart, 19 December 1974, and 28 May–1 June 1980.

Avocet *Recurvirostra avosetta*

Winter visitor and passage-migrant; very rare and local.

First recorded in the Parrett Estuary, 30 July 1939. Wintering there regularly from 1952; usually single birds, but up to five together, arriving August/early September and departing February–April. Much scarcer from May to July; usually isolated records of two to four birds. Highest count of nine, 4 December 1982, but since 1980 only a handful of isolated records and no long-staying wintering birds, in contrast to the increase in the British breeding population. However, eight resting on the water off Porlock on 3 December 1987, and three in the Parrett Estuary the same day were the largest flocks for some years.

Single records from the Axe Estuary and Porlock Marsh; twice at Durleigh Reservoir. Elsewhere, three single birds at Cheddar Reservoir: 18 December 1969, 22–26 October 1970, and 4 September 1976.

One ringed bird at Sutton Bingham Reservoir, 14 November 1983.

Stone-curlew *Burhinus oedicnemus*

Formerly occasional visitor; now vagrant.

Apparently a not uncommon autumn visitor to the Mendips before 1900, when its breeding range was much more widespread in north-west Europe; Mathew had observed flocks of up to 12 passing over, in the neighbourhood of Buckland Dinham. Also a number of winter records involving single birds.

Records since 1900 are all of single birds: Minehead, 4 April 1912; Wedmore, 20 August 1927; Lyng, mid-February 1930; Steart, August 1952; Steart, six dates, 17 September–28 October 1973; Lilstock, 8 October 1978; Wall Common, 31 July 1981.

Cream-coloured Courser   *Cursorius cursor*

Vagrant.

One record: one, Minehead Golf Course, 24–26 September 1941.

Collared Pratincole   *Glareola pratincola*

Vagrant.

One record before 1858 on North Mendips (so possibly in Avon).

Black-winged Pratincole   *Glareola nordmanni*

Vagrant.

Two records of single birds: Steart, 15 June 1957; near Ilchester, 8 September 1968.

Little Ringed Plover   *Charadrius dubius*

Passage-migrant; annual in irregular numbers.

First recorded at Durleigh Reservoir, 14 August 1952. Five records of six birds, 1956–65, then annually from 1966 in increasing numbers, particularly from 1970, since when has occurred at both seasons annually. Most recorded at the reservoirs; occasional on coast and levels.

In spring, earliest 26 March and latest 28 May; most mid-April–early May. Maximum count, seven, Cheddar Reservoir, 3 May 1974; average of at least four per spring, 1970–86.

Single birds, Berrow, 18 June 1981, and Sutton Bingham Reservoir, 21 June 1986, precede main autumn passage, 28 June–18 October. Most pass through in August, but in some years passage is later than in others. Maximum count, 15, Cheddar Reservoir, 10 August 1976; average of at least 11 per autumn, 1970–86. Of birds aged, adults tend to be mainly in July and August.

Ringed Plover   *Charadrius hiaticula*

Passage-migrant; locally common. Winter visitor; uncommon and local. Summer visitor; rare and local.

Breeds on sandy, shingle or shell beaches, and is subject to much human disturbance. Formerly nested on Steart Island; usually seven to nine nests, maximum 11 in 1933. From that peak there appears to have been a sharp decline to one or two pairs until 1946, and then did not breed again until 1984. Up to three pairs regularly between Steart and Stolford. Irregular at Porlock Marsh, where probably last bred in 1981, and the last pair at Berrow was in 1974, after some years' absence.

Passage and wintering birds mainly in the Parrett Estuary from Berrow to Stolford; small numbers in Axe Estuary and in the west. Autumn passage, consisting of both the nominate race from Britain, Iceland and Greenland, and the north European race *C.h. tundrae*, from mid-July to early October; peak numbers mid-August–early September. Counts of up to 500 in August in the Parrett Estuary, but during the 1970s total counts in the area indicated up to 2000 birds. Occurs in small parties at the reservoirs, with maxima of 50 at Durleigh, 1 September 1980; 48 at Sutton Bingham, 17 August 1975; and 45 at Cheddar, 31 August 1976.

Although some British birds move to the Continent, some remain to winter and these are joined by birds from the Wadden Sea and Baltic coasts; probably less than 200 winter in the county.

Spring passage from late April to early June, sometimes earlier, with peak in mid-May. Normally up to 150 but exceptionally 1000, as at Berrow, 20 May 1973, and at Steart in May 1977.

On the levels, only two autumn records, with small numbers in spring when fields are flooded, early March–mid-June; maxima of 25 on Blackford Moor, 12 March 1966; 14 at Witcombe Bottom, 15 May 1977; and nine on Wet Moor, 10 June 1979.

Kentish Plover   *Charadrius alexandrinus*

Vagrant.

An old record of one at Burnham, before 1893. More recently, nine records of ten birds: single birds, Porlock Marsh, 19 April 1956; Steart, 20 August 1966; Minehead, 10–12 November 1968; Berrow, 10 June 1971, 19 May

1973; Axe Estuary, 9 October 1976; two males, Berrow 15/16 April 1981; one in winter plumage, West Huntspill, 7 October 1983; one, Brue Estuary, 19 March 1988.

Dotterel   *Charadrius morinellus*

Passage-migrant; rare.

Before the decline in the late nineteenth century, said to have occurred fairly frequently on passage on the Mendips, where most records were of shot birds.

Five records of up to three birds, 1937–65, with an increase from the late 1960s, in line with the national trend.

One record from Steart, one or two on Minehead Golf Course, but most on moors covered in short heather or tussocky grass on high ground. On the Mendips from Bristol Plain Farm near Priddy to Crook Peak and Brean Down; one record at Crowcombe Park Gate on Quantocks; but most from Exmoor, especially Dunkery Hill.

Since 1969, reported in the spring from 25 April to 18 May; eight records of 54 birds; several groups of up to nine, but one of 22, Chains Barrow, 25 April 1984.

In autumn, nine single birds and two records of three, 16 August–19 September, with a late bird on Dunkery, 27 October 1986.

In 1988 a bird stayed on Fenning Island, Steart from 28 August to early September.

American Golden Plover   *Pluvialis dominica*

Vagrant.

Two records: a winter-plumaged bird, Steart, 23/24 September 1973; in 1984, an adult moulting from summer plumage on Stoke Moor, 4–8 October, and at Tealham Moor on 5th, before moving to Cheddar Reservoir, from 9th to 26th.

Golden Plover *Pluvialis apricaria*

Winter visitor and passage-migrant; locally common. Has bred.

Southern limits of the breeding distribution have markedly contracted since the mid-nineteenth century. Bred on Black Down, 1901, and probably on Exmoor in 1910. A few recent May records from Exmoor are of late passage birds, which may form pairs.

In winter, arrives in variable numbers: occasionally over 1000, rarely more than 2000, and once 6000, at Minehead, 21 January 1967. Numbers at Minehead have been greatly reduced in recent years. Wintering birds tend to avoid land above 200m, at least in colder weather, and favoured fields are typically shared with Lapwings and Black-headed Gulls. Up to 3000 on Tealham Moor in January, with up to 2000 on West Sedge Moor in March. Moves to the coast in hard weather and may leave the area altogether if freezing conditions persist.

March numbers are bolstered by the Icelandic population returning north. April counts of up to 700 at Minehead and on West Sedge Moor, and regularly up to 330 on Exmoor. Stragglers into May; two June records on the coast; one 'northern' bird at Cheddar Reservoir, 29 June–mid-September 1984; and one summered on the levels in 1977.

Occasional in July and August. First main arrival on coast and Exmoor from mid-September to November, but scarce elsewhere till October.

Birds of the so-called 'northern type' are seen in March and April, when readily identifiable in breeding plumage, and they probably account for many of the earlier birds in autumn.

Regarded as an uncommon visitor to the reservoirs and only when areas of dry mud available; a maximum of 74, Cheddar Reservoir, 10 November 1984. Some movement noted between certain areas: the flock that contained the American Golden Plover moved between Stoke and Tealham Moors and Cheddar Reservoir.

Grey Plover *Pluvialis squatarola*

Winter visitor and passage-migrant; locally fairly common.

Occurs mostly in the Parrett Estuary from Berrow to Stolford, although irregular in numbers. Scarce elsewhere: up to 200 in the Axe Estuary; maximum of 22, Dunster–Minehead, in January, and infrequent at Porlock.

In winter, generally fewer than 100 in the Parrett Estuary, but from late 1970s increased from 220, January 1977, to a record count of 533, February 1983. Numbers have dropped to previous levels since, the peak being explained by a series of good breeding seasons in Arctic Russia.

Wintering birds depart in early March, others passing through from early April to mid-May. Up to 60, presumably first-year non-breeding birds, have summered in the Parrett Estuary.

Adults start passing southwards from mid-July to mid-September, joined by juveniles from then on; autumn counts of up to 400 in August and September during the 1970s, but 400, 1 November 1973, was unusual. Numbers now usually less then 200.

Occasional inland, mostly at Cheddar Reservoir, with 18 records of 29 birds; maximum of six juveniles, 16–20 September 1984. Also at Sutton Bingham: five records of ten birds, including six, 29 May 1983. Reported in all periods except June–29 July; most from mid-September to early October. Rare on the levels: seven single birds, and two records of two; exceptionally, 30 on Tadham Moor, 28 February 1966. Not yet recorded in the east of the county.

Lapwing *Vanellus vanellus*

Resident, summer visitor and winter visitor, passage-migrant; locally very common.

As a breeding bird, very little information before 1900, but probably fairly common. Formerly nested on Steart Island: four pairs noted in 1920, then in small numbers till the 1950s. One nest, containing four eggs, was constructed in tidal debris, Stolford, 18 May 1926. One to three pairs nested on Fenning Island till the 1960s. Elsewhere, noted as increasing on the Central Levels in the 1920s and widely distributed by 1950. The *Breeding Atlas* shows pairs present in every square, with breeding confirmed in 43 squares, probable in six and possible in three. The Somerset Levels Survey in 1983 located 340 pairs, with a further 35 elsewhere. The most important areas are Tealham and Tadham Moors, Butleigh and Walton Moors, North Moor (Aller) and Lyng Hitchings, West Sedge Moor, Greylake–Beer, Kennard, South and Butt Moors. Numbers may vary considerably from year to year and, although they prefer areas of short or sparse vegetation, unlike other breeding waders they are not dependent on wet ground, though this may provide a more accessible food supply than drier fields. Ultimately, drainage of damp meadows and reclamation of waste ground, with the repeated use of machinery for cultivation early in the nesting season, may affect the lowland breeding population.

Large post-breeding flocks of up to 6300 on Wet Moor and 5000 on Tealham Moor, with smaller flocks elsewhere, occur in June and July, being mostly of Continental origin. Summer movements merge into autumn migration during September to November as juveniles leave the breeding grounds. Some wintering birds are British-bred but most are from Scandinavia, Denmark, Holland and Germany. Peak wintering numbers from November to February, with up to 25,000 on West Sedge Moor, 14,000 at Witcombe Bottom and North Moor, and over 10,000 on Muchelney Level, Othery and Tealham Moor, but numbers are variable and often dependent on Continental weather.

In freezing conditions birds move to the coast where up to 20,000 were at Berrow, 8 January 1982. Hard-weather movements are noted regularly, often involving thousands of birds, and in prolonged icy spells birds may leave the area completely, as happened in 1986 when only four were reported, 15 February–6 March. Return movements less spectacular as flocks disperse from March to mid-April.

A chick ringed at Steart, 2 June 1929, was recovered near Dax (Landes), France, 8 March 1934.

Knot   *Calidris canutus*

Winter visitor and passage-migrant; locally common, but irregular. Has summered.

Before 1930 a few autumn and winter records from Bridgwater Bay. Observed more regularly, especially since 1955, with wintering flocks 1000–4000 in the early 1960s. Since then, wintering numbers variable and highest counts often on passage. Most birds prefer the Parrett Estuary though up to 1800 have occurred in the Axe Estuary, but only infrequent and in small numbers elsewhere on the coast on passage. Since 1980, the highest counts have been between 300 and 650.

Most wintering birds depart in February or March. Spring passage very light, April–early June. Autumn arrival and passage dates very irregular, from mid-July to November, with peak passage after September.

Inland, apart from 60 at Durleigh, 11/12 October 1987, and 40 there 13 October 1963, appears occasionally and usually singly at the reservoirs, particularly Cheddar; mostly August–November, with single records February, April, July and December.

One old record away from the reservoirs, at Nynehead, and more recently 12 on flooded pasture, Tadham Moor, 28 February 1966, and one, Stoke Moor, 22 January 1968.

Sanderling   *Calidris alba*

Passage-migrant and winter visitor; uncommon and local.

The main site is Berrow, with a few birds in the Parrett Estuary; irregular in small numbers in the Axe Estuary and in the west at Dunster/Minehead. Formerly up to 40 wintered Brean–Burnham and at Dunster Beach, but from the mid-1970s very rare December/January, with a maximum of four in January 1980. The wintering population is of Siberian origin and is subject to periodic fluctuation; in years of relative scarcity of Lemmings, the Sanderling suffers from predation by Arctic Foxes.

Passage birds belong to the Greenland population that winters in Africa; spring passage mainly mid-April–late May, with most in May; usually 10–150, but 350, 19 May 1969; a few in early June. In 1987, none were reported on spring passage, for the first time in at least 25 years.

Autumn passage mid-July–late October/early November, mostly late July–mid-August; numbers variable: up to 300 recorded in late July, but usually 40 to 220.

Occurs on passage at the reservoirs: since 1966, 84 per cent of the records at Cheddar Reservoir, five at Sutton Bingham, two at Durleigh and one at Chard. In the period 1966–86, 31 records of 75 birds; spring extremes, 30

April–7 June; maximum of six at Cheddar Reservoir, 6 May 1980. Autumn passage: 17 records, 30 July–11 September, with very noticeable peaks late July to mid-August and end of August–early September, presumably adults followed by juveniles. At Cheddar, one record of two in October; single birds in November and December.

Semipalmated Sandpiper   *Calidris pusilla*

Vagrant.

One or two records, both for Sutton Bingham Reservoir: a bird there, 18–21 October 1973, was submitted as a Semipalmated Sandpiper, but was accepted by the *British Birds* Rarities Committee as either that species or Western Sandpiper *Calidris mauri*; a juvenile, 2–7 October 1982.

Little Stint   *Calidrus minuta*

Passage-migrant; rare in spring, scarce and local in autumn. Exceptional in winter.

Most records from Berrow to Steart, a few Dunster/Minehead and Porlock; regular at the reservoirs, particularly Cheddar; fewer at Sutton Bingham and Durleigh. Exceptional on the levels: seven records of ten birds in autumn, and two single birds, 2 March and 18 May.

In spring, 11 birds, 12 April–25 May, and one on 5 June; all but two records from the Parrett Estuary.

In autumn, apart from one on 13 July, passage from 27 July to 29 November; an influx in the last week of August, and peak numbers mid- to late September; uncommon after mid-October, scarce in November. Numbers vary from year to year from a few to as many as 100 in outstanding years. Usually singly or in small parties but up to 90 at Berrow, late September 1960; 49 there, 30 September 1967, and 27, 30 September 1973. Inland, up to 14 at Cheddar (24 September 1967).

Three winter records, 1935–49, but since 1974 at least 22 birds, 11 December–14 March, all in the Parrett Estuary, except one on Tadham Moor, 2 March 1978. A maximum of four in December 1985; although small, the wintering population in Britain is at the extreme north-western edge of the range, and has increased in recent years.

Temminck's Stint   *Calidris temminckii*

Passage migrant; very rare.

Three old records: four shot from six, Brue Estuary, September 1805; one, North Curry, 14 November 1874; three, Cheddar Reservoir, 4 June 1939.

More recently, seven records of eight birds since 1970: one, Cheddar Reservoir, 28–31 August 1970; two, King's Moor, 23 March 1972; single birds, Porlock Marsh, 13 September 1972; Cheddar Reservoir, 28 May 1975 and 1976; Sutton Bingham, 29–31 July 1982, and an adult there, 6–10 September 1984.

White-rumped Sandpiper   *Calidris fuscicollis*

Vagrant.

Three records: one, Cheddar Reservoir, 9–16 August 1976; an adult, West Huntspill, 29 July, 14–16 August 1984; a juvenile, Cheddar Reservoir, 16–28 October 1987.

Baird's Sandpiper   *Calidris bairdii*

Vagrant.

Two records of single birds: Porlock Marsh, 15 September 1973, and Steart, 15 September 1974.

Pectoral Sandpiper   *Calidris melanotos*

Passage-migrant; very rare.

First record at Porlock Marsh, 6 September–13 October 1947. Three further records to 1954, then reported in 13 years out of 20 from 1968 to 1987.

One spring record: Porlock Marsh, 5 May 1974.

In autumn, probably 27 birds, 28 July–31 October; mostly late August–

mid-October, with peak in mid-September. Reported at the following localities in autumn: Cheddar Reservoir (11), Parrett Estuary (nine), Durleigh (four), Porlock, Sutton Bingham Reservoir (two each), Minehead, Axe Estuary and inland at Creech St Michael (one each).

Usually singly, with two records of two together, and possibly as many as seven individuals in 1984.

Curlew Sandpiper   *Calidris ferruginea*

Passage-migrant; scarce and local.

Before 1900, six autumn and undated records on coast between Burnham and Porlock. One shot on 'Sedge Moor', about Christmas 1876, remains the only inland record away from the reservoirs.

In spring, 13 birds: once March, the rest 22 April–20 June; all on the coast and mostly in the Parrett Estuary.

In autumn, reported more regularly in recent years, but numbers vary from year to year; sometimes only single figures but in years when weather displaces continental migrants, over 100 may occur, as in 1969 and 1978. Passage from 23 July to 21 November, with a small peak July–mid-August. In some years a large influx, mainly of juveniles, occurs late August–mid-September, decreasing by early October; a few till late November. Highest counts: 86, Steart, 11 September 1969, with 33 there, 10 September 1978, and at Durleigh, 3 September 1972. Most occur in the Parrett Estuary and at Berrow, with small numbers Axe Estuary, Dunster/Minehead and Porlock.

In winter, besides the 'Sedge Moor' record, once at Steart, 9 January 1965.

Inland, most at Cheddar Reservoir, where a maximum of 14, 7 September 1981; fewer at Durleigh, and scarce at Sutton Bingham.

Purple Sandpiper   *Calidris maritima*

Passage-migrant and winter visitor; rare and local.

Recorded in all months except June and July, mainly from Brean Down and the coast from Watchet to Minehead; a few from the Parrett Estuary, and once at Kilve.

Spring passage from late March to 14 May, returning from 1 August to September; some overlap with wintering records, mostly from mid-October to early March. Normally ones or twos; four records of three, and three of four; maximum counts at Brean Down of five, 21 October 1981, and six, 4 May 1974.

Inland, single birds at Cheddar Reservoir, 12–24 December 1969 and 8 November 1987, and at Brent Knoll Services, M5, 24 January 1982.

Dunlin   *Calidris alpina*

Passage-migrant and winter visitor; common. Has bred.

Bred on Exmoor before 1887. A pair displayed near Simonsbath, May 1931, and one displayed in 'West Somerset', 7 June 1934; no recent records.

Frequent on passage and in winter on all parts of the coastline, with by far the largest flocks in Bridgwater Bay. Smaller numbers in the Axe Estuary, at Dunster/Minehead and Porlock.

Wintering birds leave in late February and early March. Spring passage March–late May, with a peak late April–mid-May; a maximum of 4000 at Steart during the 1960s; often up to 2000, but only 100 in 1986. Scarce from early June.

Return passage from early or mid-July to late November, with a peak mid-August–mid-September; many of these birds pass through before the main arrival of the wintering birds in October and November. Regularly up to 15,000 in Bridgwater Bay, and 4000 in the Axe Estuary, although 7000 there, 24 December 1971; scarcer in the west. Between 15,000 and 30,000 may be present in Somerset during the winter months.

Ringing data suggests that passage birds are almost entirely of the north-west European and Greenland races *C.a. schinzii* and *C.a. arctica*, and that the vast majority of wintering birds are the north Scandinavian and Russian race *C.a. alpina* with a few *schinzii*. Juveniles arriving in autumn at the Severn Estuary stay there to winter and return there each year. Significant differences have been noted in the feeding ecology of males (short-billed birds) and females (long-billed birds), and the sex ratio is quite marked, dependent on the available feeding areas (Clark, 1983).

Inland, very small numbers in spring; more numerous in autumn, with nocturnal passage frequently reported. Regular at the reservoirs, particularly when mud available, with a high count of 410 at Cheddar, November/December 1973. On the levels, occasional on passage but regular November to February in variable numbers, often dependent on flooding; a maximum of 2000 on West Sedge Moor, 13–16 February 1975.

Broad-billed Sandpiper   *Limicola falcinellus*

Vagrant.

One record: Sutton Bingham Reservoir, 5/6 September 1973.

Buff-breasted Sandpiper   *Tryngites subruficollis*

Vagrant.

First reported at Steart, 18 September 1966, and ten further records, 28 July and 19 August–7 November: single records from July, August and November, five in September, three October. Six from Cheddar Reservoir, four from Steart and once at Sutton Bingham Reservoir.

Ruff   *Philomachus pugnax*

Passage-migrant and winter visitor; locally fairly common.

Ruff certainly occurred and may have bred on the levels before 1800, but there is no proof of this. Only ten reported, 1853–1903, with about 300 from then till 1965, increasing rapidly after 1950.

In winter, singly or small parties but an increase in February and March attributed to part of a small European wintering population that moves north early in the year; this was most apparent in the mid-1970s when over 300 on West Sedge Moor, 29 February 1976, and about 190 on Tealham Moor, 14 February 1976. Flocks now generally less than 30.

Small spring passage late March to June, with a peak in April, when birds occur more widely on the coast and at the reservoirs.

Occasional June records before main autumn passage from late July to early November, with most in early September. Occurs mainly in the Parrett Estuary, at Cheddar and Durleigh Reservoirs, on the Central Levels, and occasionally elsewhere. Maximum counts: 35, King's Moor, 10 October 1976; 32, Steart, 26 September 1973; 15, Cheddar Reservoir, 22 August 1976 and 23 September 1980.

Jack Snipe   *Lymnocryptes minimus*

Winter visitor and passage-migrant; local.

Occurs mainly in wetter parts of the levels, or marsh-fringed reservoirs and coastal *Spartina*, more rarely in marshy areas on the Mendips and Exmoor.

A few pass through from early August to September, but main influx from mid-October. Wintering birds depart in March, and some spring passage March–mid-April; occasional late April, three in early May.

Usually singly or in parties of up to five, occasionally ten, but up to 15 at Dunster and Long Load, with 25 on King's Moor, 24 December 1974, and 50 at Shapwick, 18 November 1960.

Snipe   *Gallinago gallinago*

Resident, passage-migrant and winter visitor; locally common.

Formerly more common as a breeding bird. Scarce on Exmoor, where up to 20 pairs reported in 1978. Last bred on Mendips in 1915, on Quantocks before 1865, and bred on the Blackdowns till about 1936. Breeds locally on the South and Central Levels, especially on the peat-moors; recent surveys suggest a continued decline south of the Poldens, with some small increase on the peat-moors. Snipe appear to be particularly sensitive to the effects of drainage and subsequent habitat change. The drainage on King's Moor

during the 1970s reduced the number of pairs by 90 per cent to only one in 1983. In the same year, West Sedge Moor held the highest breeding density (4.8 pairs/sq.km), which is low when compared with other major sites. Nevertheless, the levels still held 7.5 per cent of lowland-breeding Snipe, and 44 per cent of those in south-west England.

On passage and in winter common on the levels, floods, marshes and reservoirs, and in coastal *Spartina*. Autumn passage from late July to mid-November in variable numbers. The number of wintering birds is dependent on the prevalence of standing water on the levels, and on the effects of cold weather both here and on the Continent. The winter of 1976/77 in particular had large numbers: King's Moor held 6500 on 26 December, with 3500 still there on 3 March. In icy conditions birds may be found in any areas of open water including the coast, springs on hillsides and roadside drains, and also feeding in gardens and other open areas.

In spring, small passage from March to early April; difficult to detect due to the secretive nature of this species in early spring.

Great Snipe *Gallinago media*

Vagrant.

Besides five old published records that cannot be safely authenticated, there are acceptable records from Wedmore before 1900, and Tealham Moor, 'winter 1906'. More recently, one, Cheddar Clay-Pits, 3 April 1949.

Long-billed Dowitcher *Limnodromus griseus*

Vagrant.

The first two of the five records of single birds were identified only as 'Dowitcher sp.': Steart Point, 24 October 1965, and Steart Island, 25 October 1970; Porlock Marsh, 29 September–26 October 1973; Sutton Bingham Reservoir, 8–22 October 1977; Steart, 13 January 1978.

Woodcock *Scolopax rusticola*

Winter visitor and passage-migrant; locally common. Rare breeder.

This elusive bird is undoubtedly under-recorded, and probably occurs fairly commonly and widely during winter months. The majority of records are from deciduous woodland on the hills and in the Exmoor combes. Very rarely recorded from the South Levels; a few from Shapwick, Westhay Moor and Street Heath, which are mainly peat-moors with areas of ash and birch scrubland.

Hard-weather influxes and icy conditions drive birds into the open and towards the coast; such an influx in very cold weather brought up to 50 to the Burnham/West Huntspill area in late February and early March 1986. When details of shooting parties and estate records are analysed, perhaps a more accurate reflection of relative abundance becomes apparent; for example, 11 shot at Cricket St Thomas, 13 November 1974, and 20 seen in a day at Orchard Portman, early December 1984.

Passage from mid-October (earliest 9th), with main influx November, mainly of Scandinavian birds. Departure in late February and March, with a few April records. April and September records may relate to prospective breeders or summering birds. Breeding suspected and occasionally proved in very small numbers throughout the county: most regular at Gare Hill, which straddles the Wiltshire border; once at Copley Wood; roding birds in eight summers since 1970 at Shapwick; two pairs regular at Dinnington till at least 1981; probably regular at Norton-sub-Hamdon; bred at Bridgetown in 1981 and on Staple Common in 1982.

Black-tailed Godwit *Limosa limosa*

Passage-migrant; local. Winter visitor; scarce. Rare breeder.

Most records are in the autumn from the Parrett Estuary, with some movement between here and Durleigh Reservoir; occasional high counts from the Axe Estuary, and a few scattered records inland at the reservoirs and on the levels, but very scarce elsewhere, with only occasional records of single birds at Minehead and Porlock in autumn.

Only reported in nine years before 1940. Annually since then, increasing particularly from the late 1950s, with the highest numbers during the 1970s, but has decreased since 1980.

Wintering birds are of Icelandic origin (*L.l. islandica*); they depart from February, with the main passage, including the nominate race, from April to early May. Usually less than 150; some birds, presumably first-years, occasionally summer. Return passage from mid-July to September, with peak in late July/early August; most leave in October, a few remaining to winter. In the 1970s, highest counts 650–1800 in July/August, with a record 2200 in July 1977; returning to 650 in 1979 but decreasing to as low as 33 in 1986. Maximum count from the Axe Estuary: 450, 16 November 1969.

Breeding first recorded on the levels in 1963, then annually from 1969, increasing from one pair to up to eight in 1980 when Somerset held 10–13 per cent of Britain's breeding population. Breeding success very poor since 1982.

Inland on passage, up to 158 on the levels in March/April during the 1970s; now much scarcer. In autumn and early winter, an irregular flock at Durleigh Reservoir, where up to 300, 13 December 1975. Elsewhere, regular in small numbers at the other reservoirs, July–October, mostly late August/early September; maxima of 12 at Cheddar, 9 September 1985, and six at Sutton Bingham, 4 August 1969.

Bar-tailed Godwit   *Limosa lapponica*

Passage-migrant; irregular and local. Winter visitor; scarce and very local.

Occurs on the coast from Axe Estuary to Stolford, and from Blue Anchor to Minehead; most common in the Parrett Estuary, but rare at Porlock Marsh and inland.

In spring, usually early March–late May or early June, most late April/ early May. Very irregular, from 400 in May 1966 to only one in April/May 1983. An exceptional influx in 1984, with 2100 on 28 April, was presumably part of the West African wintering population that migrate up the English Channel to moult in the Wadden Sea, here deflected by easterly winds. Scarce in June, but up to 280 have occurred, presumably non-breeding birds.

Return passage, mid- or late July–October, with peak at any time during this period. Up to 250 in Parrett Estuary 17 July; a general though variable decline noted since 1978 with only one count in three figures (108, July 1984). During late 1960s, up to 150 wintered; now scarce, with a maximum count of 21 since 1982.

Inland, at the reservoirs: ten, Durleigh, 4 November 1984, and five records of eight birds there, 12 October–18 January; Cheddar, four single birds, 22 August–7 November; Sutton Bingham, single birds, 16 May 1983 and 28 October 1984. Twelve records of up to 58 birds away from the reservoirs, mostly April/May, once each January and August; largest count of 35, flying over Langport, 1 May 1981.

Whimbrel   *Numenius phaeopus*

Passage-migrant; fairly common locally in spring, scarcer in autumn.

The average first date, 1924–65, was 26 April, with three March records, the earliest on 21st. Since then the average first date has been 11 April, and all but three dates have been before the 26th; again, three March records.

Most of the flocks pass in last week of April/early May, with a few up to 25 May, and odd birds through June. These are considered to be birds of the Icelandic breeding population *en route* from African wintering quarters (Ferns, Green & Round, 1979).

Flocks feed by day on the levels, favouring those with high water tables and rough, grazed fields with tussocks. Since 1972, flocks have been noted roosting at Steart, but some may remain on the levels if wet conditions persist. Birds are suspected to stay in the area for several days before moving on, and therefore Somerset is an important 'refuelling' area; continuous drainage and upgrading of fields pose a threat to this species. From peak counts of 1978 in 1973 and 1800 in 1977, numbers were down to only 122 in 1985, and 686 in 1987. For a study of this passage, see Slade and McGeoch (1979).

In autumn, earliest 1 July, most in August–mid-September; occasional stragglers into October; four times in November, the latest on 10th. Much smaller numbers than in spring, with peak counts of 275 in August in Parrett Estuary, up to 60 at Charterhouse, 21 July 1979, and 45 near Cheddar Reservoir, 31 July 1986. One winter record: Minehead, 26 December 1927.

Curlew   *Numenius arquata*

Passage-migrant and winter visitor; locally common. Summer visitor; local.

Most breeders and all those on hills are summer visitors arriving from mid- or late March. Breeds on Exmoor, both on grass and heather moorland. Numbers irregular, but no general survey has been undertaken. In 1978, up to 35 pairs, but probably fewer in most years, and may have declined. One or two pairs regular on Blackdown Hills. Has bred on Mendips: last definite record in 1928, but several recent summer records. On the levels, first recorded breeding on Queen's Sedge Moor in 1900, more regular from 1920s, especially since 1945. A total of 57 pairs in 1972, with main sites on West Sedge Moor and Greylake–Beer. Some decrease noted in recent years, particularly along the Brue Valley and on adjacent heaths – presumably due to drainage and loss of habitat.

Passage and wintering birds concentrated mainly in the Parrett Estuary, the Axe Estuary and Minehead, with small numbers elsewhere. Main arrival from mid-July, when up to 2000 have occurred; most from August to November, when up to 1500 in Parrett Estuary and exceptionally 500 at Minehead. Up to 350 in the Axe Estuary, mainly December–February. Numbers variable from year to year; scarcer 1969–74 (maximum about 600), and scarcer in the west, where now a maximum of 250 between Dunster and Minehead, and 170 at Porlock, July to March.

Birds leave in early March and others pass on coasts and inland till early May; most are gone by mid-April. Small numbers on coast, May/June, but 250 at Steart, 30 May 1953, were probably non-breeding summer visitors.

Upland Sandpiper   *Bartramia longicauda*

Vagrant.

One very old record: a bird shot in winter at Combwich or 'Turf Moor' (i.e. on the peat-moors), before 1854.

Spotted Redshank   *Tringa erythropus*

Passage-migrant; scarce and local. Winter visitor; rare.

Only seven reports before 1946, then 190 or more individuals 1947–66; more frequent since. Most records from the Parrett Estuary and Durleigh Reservoir; regular Cheddar and Sutton Bingham Reservoirs, and Axe Estuary; occasionally on the levels and elsewhere, including Porlock Marsh.

Much more common in autumn than in spring; usually from early July to late October, but has occurred in June in the Parrett Estuary: two, 13 June 1984, and four, 15 June 1970. Usually singly or in small parties, but in the Parrett Estuary high counts of 60, 30 August 1981; 35, 13 October 1984; and 30 or more, 17 September 1978. Inland, up to ten at Cheddar Reservoir (25 August 1980, 21 September 1980), nine at Durleigh (14 September 1968), and six at Sutton Bingham (13 September 1969).

November records may still be of late migrants, but in more recent years birds have wintered, with regular counts in the Brue and Huntspill Estuaries of up to 11 birds, December–March. Occasional, but rare, on the levels in winter; all records are of single birds from wetter moors.

March records may be late wintering birds, but a definite peak in second half of April; virtually all records are in the Parrett Estuary, where occasionally up to ten. Rare elsewhere: one or two at Porlock Marsh, and single birds on the wetter levels.

Redshank   *Tringa totanus*

Resident or summer visitor; local. Also passage-migrant and winter visitor; locally common.

Formerly only a passage-migrant and scarce winter visitor on the coast; with westward expansion of breeding range, first bred at Axe Estuary and Steart around 1900. By 1930 had spread to many parts of the peat-moors, King's Sedge Moor, and Steart Island. The numbers of inland breeding pairs are dependent on the availability of damp feeding areas, but densities are generally poor. In the wet summer of 1983, 62 pairs bred on the levels, but with continual drainage the trend is inevitably downward. The only regular coastal site now is Porlock Marsh, which holds up to six pairs.

In autumn, passage from late June to November, with the peak in late July and August; numbers variable, but up to 1400 have occurred in August and October in the Parrett Estuary. Wintering birds, considered to be mainly of the Icelandic race *T.t. robusta*, are generally found in the Parrett and Axe Estuaries, with up to 950 in the former and 500 in the latter; only small numbers elsewhere, and on the flooded levels.

Inland, passage birds and prospective breeders appear during February, and up to 80 have occurred on Wet Moor. Exceptional in the east, mainly on passage at Emborough Pond and Orchardleigh. Small numbers at the reservoirs on passage: mainly ones or twos or up to seven, so 19 at Leigh Reservoir, 10 November 1985, was unusual.

Marsh Sandpiper   *Tringa stagnatilis*

Vagrant.

One record: a juvenile, Cheddar Reservoir, 20 August 1984, later moved to Chew Valley Lake and Blagdon Reservoir (Avon).

Greenshank   *Tringa nebularia*

Passage-migrant; locally fairly common in autumn, scarce in spring. Winter visitor; rare.

Occurs mainly at Cheddar, Durleigh and Sutton Bingham Reservoirs, on the coast from Axe Estuary to Stolford, particularly in the Parrett Estuary, and at Minehead and Porlock Marsh. Also in ones or twos on the levels, at less favoured reservoirs and elsewhere; rarely on Exmoor.

Usually early July (occasionally late June) to late October, rarely to mid-November. Peak mid-August–early September, when mainly juveniles pass through. Highest counts include: 25, Cheddar Reservoir, 22 August 1976; 20, Parrett Estuary, 6 September 1979, 5 October 1968; 17, Sutton Bingham Reservoir, 24 August 1976.

Only three December records, so small number of reports January–mid-February are presumably migrants returning early from their wintering areas.

Less common in spring. Main passage early/mid-April–mid-/late May; occasional in June, with latest on 12th; the timing of this passage would suggest birds of the Fenno-Scandinavian breeding population. Occurs mostly in the Parrett Estuary, occasionally at Cheddar and Durleigh Reservoirs, and Porlock Marsh, rarely elsewhere, including the levels; usually ones or twos, but up to five recorded.

Green Sandpiper   *Tringa ochropus*

Passage-migrant; locally common. Winter visitor; scarce and local.

Occurs widely throughout the county, although mostly in central areas, and very rare in the east. Found by suitable waters, rhynes and pools on the levels, on the muddier reservoirs, and on coastal pools and estuaries.

Small spring passage, mid-March–late April, with seven May records.

Regular in autumn. Earliest 14 June, mostly late July–mid-September, with peak often in second week of August. Has apparently increased in recent years, with total numbers often over 100, mainly in ones and twos or small parties. Maxima of 18, Durleigh Reservoir, 19–21 August 1987, and 14, at Wells Sewage Farm, 16 August 1973, and on West Sedge Moor, 27 July 1983.

In winter, reported widely but locally from Central Levels. Occasional at Durleigh and Sutton Bingham Reservoirs and Wells Sewage Farm. Usually ones or twos, exceptionally five together.

Wood Sandpiper *Tringa glareola*

Passage-migrant; very rare in spring, scarce and local in autumn.

Only three spring records before 1965: 9–31 May. Since then, eight records of nine birds, 18 April–26 May: one in the Axe Estuary, the rest at Berrow and the Parrett Estuary.

In autumn, two old records before 1903, then 37, 1947–65; since then, four to 15 birds annually. Since 1966, once 30 June, three in mid-July; then large influx last few days of July/early August, probably mainly of adults; a second peak in last few days of August, probably juveniles. Eight records of stragglers in October up to 14th.

Most frequent at Durleigh, Cheddar and Sutton Bingham Reservoirs, and Porlock Marsh, fewer at Berrow and the Parrett Estuary, with small numbers at Wimbleball and occasionally at other reservoirs, sewage farms and pools on the levels.

Maximum counts of six, at Porlock, 30 July 1972, and Durleigh, 8 August 1970. Up to four at Cheddar Reservoir, 22 and 28 August 1976, and Wimbleball, 28 August 1978.

Terek Sandpiper *Xenus cinereus*

Vagrant.

One record: an adult in summer plumage, Sutton Bingham Reservoir, 18 August 1974.

Common Sandpiper *Actitis hypoleucos*

Passage-migrant; locally common. Has bred; now occasional summer visitor. Winter visitor; scarce and local.

Bred fairly regularly on the River Barle between Simonsbath and Dulverton, and on the River Exe near Exford till 1920, and possibly in 1940 and 1958. Also on Godney Moor, 1898/99 and 1930/31, and possibly near Stogursey, 1953.

On passage occurs widely throughout the county, at reservoirs and other waters, along rivers, streams and rhynes, and at coastal pools and backwaters, although scarce in the east. On spring passage, rare in March (earliest on 5th), most arriving from early April to late May, occasionally June; peak in late April. Highest count of 59 on 25 April 1954 at Cheddar Reservoir, where consistently high counts received.

Autumn passage more protracted, from mid-June to mid-October, occasionally mid-November; highest count, 53 at Clatworthy Reservoir, 14 July 1979.

Passage birds often of Scandinavian origin, as indicated by one controlled at Sutton Bingham Reservoir, 22 August 1975, which had been ringed as a first-year bird, Amager, Denmark, 15 August 1962.

Spotted Sandpiper *Actitis macularia*

Vagrant.

One record: an adult in breeding plumage, Durleigh Reservoir, 27 August–4 September 1968.

Turnstone *Arenaria interpres*

Passage-migrant and winter visitor; local.

Found mainly on the mud and shingle beaches all along the coast, particularly in the Parrett Estuary. Small numbers on passage at the reservoirs, mostly at Cheddar. In winter, mostly from Parrett Estuary to Hinkley Point, and from Watchet to Minehead.

Irregular on spring passage, late March–late May, occasionally early June, most late April/early May; up to 300 in April, more usually 20–160.

Autumn passage from late July to October. Peak variable, from late August to November; up to 300 noted, but often less than 200. Up to 250 in September, Dunster/Minehead. Winters in variable numbers, usually less than 130.

Inland, most at Cheddar Reservoir, 20 March–16 June and 25 July–8 November, with highest count of five, 11 May 1982.

Wilson's Phalarope *Phalaropus tricolor*

Vagrant.

Four records of single birds: Durleigh Reservoir, 1–4 October 1967; Steart, 22–30 August 1978; Cheddar Reservoir, 17–28 September 1980; Steart, 13 October 1984, and presumably the same bird at West Huntspill Treatment Works, 16–26 October.

Red-necked Phalarope *Phalaropus lobatus*

Passage-migrant; very rare.

Twelve records of single birds: King's Brompton Common, 17 September 1952; Porlock Marsh, 26 September 1957 and 11/12 October 1961; Blackford Moor, 19 September 1965; Durleigh Reservoir, 23–28 September 1968; Porlock Marsh, 28 September 1969; Porlock Weir, 13 September 1970; Durleigh Reservoir, 18 September 1976 and 16–19 August 1979; Steart, 26 September 1980 and 22 August 1982; Cheddar Reservoir, 4 September 1983.

Grey Phalarope *Phalaropus fulicarius*

Passage-migrant, or storm-vagrant; irregular in autumn. Vagrant in spring.

Twice in spring: three or four, Steart, 17 April 1934, and one, North Moor, 4 March 1977.

In autumn, usually occurs after strong westerly gales, 29 August–23 December, with most in September and October. About 60 between 1831 and 1903; only 20 on coast, the rest at many places inland, especially around Taunton. About 102, 1905–65, 69 of them on the coast. Between 1966 and 1987, about 77 occurred, almost half of these between Burnham-on-Sea and Stolford; 19 at Cheddar Reservoir, six each at Durleigh and Porlock Marsh, five at Minehead, two at Sutton Bingham and the Axe Estuary, and single birds at Ashford and Hawkridge Reservoirs, Combwich and Chilton Trinity. Usually singly, occasionally in twos, but up to seven together (Steart Point, 9 September 1974).

Pomarine Skua   *Stercorarius pomarinus*

Passage-migrant and winter visitor; rare.

Despite a recent upsurge in sea-watching there are, surprisingly, more old records than recent ones. About 25 occurred between 1847 and 1909, mostly in 1879 (when there was a nationwide influx) and 1886. A primary feather found on Minehead Golf Course in April 1947 was the only record between 1909 and 1973, since when at least 21 (possibly 27) have been seen.

Most have been on the coast, in recent years mainly in Bridgwater Bay, the exceptions being old inland records from Bridgwater, Bathpool and North Curry. The older records were all in October/November (where dated), whereas recent ones have been more scattered: nine or ten have occurred in spring, from mid-April to 31 May; in autumn, five to seven single birds, 26 August–8 November; about nine, December/January, mostly in January 1986 after a nationwide influx the previous autumn. Most recent records have been single birds, the maximum together being three, but on 16 October 1886 there were 12 off Minehead.

Arctic Skua   *Stercorarius parasiticus*

Passage-migrant, non-breeding summer visitor and winter visitor; scarce.

First recorded in 1860; 57 were noted up to 1965, mostly in the autumn on the coast.

With more persistent sea-watching, records have increased in recent years, with around 320 since 1965, and small numbers annually since 1969. Of these, 116 have been in spring from 27 March to the end of May; nearly 75 per cent between mid-April and mid-May. About 20 birds in June/July, probably wandering non-breeding immatures. Autumn passage from early August to 11 November, with a peak in the first fortnight of September accounting for 55 per cent of the autumn total of around 146. Autumn records are often associated with strong west/north-west winds as in 1980, when 40 were recorded between 3 and 19 September. In winter, only three records, all December/January; four birds, one of them dead.

About 75 per cent of all birds have been on the coast from Brean Down to Hinkley Point, including the vast majority of those in spring. The remainder have been from Hinkley Point to Porlock Bay, except for two or three at Cheddar Reservoir. There are old inland records from the River Axe, Cheddar Reservoir and near Wellington, and more recently, one over Westhay Heath, 30 June 1987.

Of the 84 where plumage-phase stated, 57 were dark-phase.

An exceptional count of 33 reported as this species off Dunster/Porlock, 10 November 1985; most of them flew west, but a flock of nine moved off high inland. However, this occurred on the same day as a small cross-country movement of Pomarine Skuas, and at a time when hundreds of Pomarine Skuas were present in the North Sea and English Channel (Fox and Aspinall, 1987). It seems likely that they were Pomarine Skuas, as very few Arctics were reported over the same period.

Long-tailed Skua   *Stercorarius longicaudus*

Vagrant.

ᴛᴀʙ.

Four occurred between 1862 and 1952, all from 18 October to 1 November, apart from one, Minehead Golf Course, 2–4 May 1947. A further seven autumn birds have been recorded since 1971, most 5–28 September, and one, 29 November 1987. Seven have been on the coast from Brean Down to Stolford; the remaining four were inland at Langford Heathfield (shot 1862), near Axbridge (shot 1903), Tealham Moor (1974), and Cheddar Reservoir (28/29 November 1987). Five of nine birds aged were adults.

Great Skua   *Stercorarius skua*

Passage-migrant and summer visitor; scarce. Winter visitor; rare.

This skua has increased dramatically in recent times, perhaps because of a trend since 1966 for more of them to follow the Atlantic coast than to use the North Sea flyway, and also because of the much larger numbers now breeding in Britain and the Faroes. Eight recorded between 1824 and 1925, with a further eight or nine from 1957 to 1965; all on the coast from Berrow to Minehead, mostly in autumn or winter, 28 August to 12 January, with two in spring.

Since 1965, some 184 have occurred. Of these, 32 have been on spring passage, 22 March–9 May, with no well-marked peak. Those from 23 May probably best included with June/July records, 31 birds in all, presumably wandering non-breeding immatures. Autumn passage from August to 24 November, involving over 100 birds, with a peak in September and most of the rest in August. There are more winter records than for other skuas: 10 to 13 have occurred, all 20 December to 20 January. Usually singly or up to three together, six being the maximum.

Of the total since 1965, over 80 per cent have been on the coast of Bridgwater Bay, including all but three spring/summer records; the remainder on the coast from St Audries Bay to Glenthorne.

Five inland: four at Cheddar Reservoir, and one over Holcombe.

Mediterranean Gull   *Larus melanocephalus*

Passage-migrant and winter visitor; scarce.

The first Somerset record was at Dunster Beach, 31 December 1956, with possibly the same bird returning on 25 September 1957. Next recorded in 1971, and has become increasingly regular since, in line with the national trend. Annual since 1978; the four most recent winter periods averaged 19 individuals, compared with five for the previous four winters.

At least 125 have occurred since 1971, half of these at Sutton Bingham Reservoir, due to the intensive gull-watching done here and to the gulls here originating on the south coast, the species' main range in Britain (Lack, 1986). They often feed here with Common Gulls in pasture. Few observers check gulls inland, but there are 12 records from Cheddar Reservoir and nine birds have been seen at other sites, four of these in the Mendip area, perhaps originating from the roost at Chew Valley Lake (Avon), where frequent watching has proved them regular. Rare on the levels. There have been 35 birds on the coast from the Axe Estuary to Hinkley Point, and seven at Dunster Beach; many of these were at roost.

Recorded in all months. At Sutton Bingham Reservoir, 70 per cent occur in November/December, very few January/February; a small peak of spring migrants in March. Elsewhere, there is a more even spread of records, though 54 per cent have been between November and February. Odd birds,

at first mainly adults, pass through from July. Records steadily increase to the winter peak and then decline from March, with first-year birds lingering or passing through in April and May. Another, less expected concentration of first-year birds occurs in autumn, but very few of this age are recorded in winter. The age distribution is as one would expect for a gull taking three years to reach maturity: just over half are adults, and there are slightly more first-year birds than second-years. Most have been seen on only one day, perhaps because they are overlooked amongst large numbers of other gulls, and since most gulls shift their feeding areas from day to day but often return to the same roost at night.

Laughing Gull *Larus atricilla*

Vagrant.

One record: a second-winter bird at Bossington Beach and Porlock Marsh, 8–10 September 1980.

Little Gull   *Larus minutus*

Passage-migrant and winter visitor; scarce and local.

Single birds before 1844 and in 1903 were the only records until 1938. From then until 1965 some 36 were seen, mostly at Cheddar Reservoir, with a few on the coast. These were mainly in the spring and winter, with a few in autumn.

Between 1965 and 1986, about 700 have occurred, reflecting a genuine increase (Hutchinson and Neath, 1978). Of these 56 per cent have been on spring passage, between early March and late May, but this is very erratic, ranging from none in 1966 to 112 in 1974. In most years there is a trickle from late March to early April, mostly of first-year birds. However, there have been several larger spring counts, 28 April–4 May, involving mostly adults, with a maximum of 86 at Cheddar Reservoir, 4 May 1974. This site and the coast from Berrow to Steart attract most of the birds in spring. Of the remainder, a significant proportion occur on nearby pits such as Combwich and Huntworth. Only six records in June and July.

About 250 on autumn passage from August until the end of November, more evenly spread in time and place than in spring, with no records of large flocks. Most pass through between mid-August and late September; juveniles predominate. Cheddar Reservoir and the coast from Brean Down to Stolford are most favoured, a few records on the coast further west, and in smaller numbers at Sutton Bingham, Durleigh and Chard Reservoirs.

About 45 recorded between December and February since 1965, mostly after 1980; the majority on the coast from Brean Down to Hinkley Point; now regular at the latter.

Only in spring influxes do adults predominate; first-year birds are most numerous in autumn. Very few second-year birds have been noted, but these are often passed off as adults.

Sabine's Gull   *Larus sabini*

Passage-migrant; rare.

Since the first in 1893, there have been 43 records; 37 of these have been since 1970. There is only one spring record: an adult at Porlock Marsh, 30 May–3 June 1953. In autumn, 34 between 27 August and 17 September, the rest till 6 November. Virtually all have occurred in strong westerly winds.

All but four records have been on the coast: one at the Axe Estuary, 29 from Berrow to Stolford, four (together) at Kilve, and three from Dunster to Porlock. Inland, three at Durleigh Reservoir, and a dead bird at Cheddar.

Up to four birds in the Parrett Estuary in early September 1988, and a juvenile at Cheddar Reservoir, 28 August 1988.

The autumn of 1983 produced about 22, part of an influx to south-west Britain after a severe gale on 2/3 September. All of these were in the Parrett Estuary, mostly on the 3rd (14 birds), and the 4th (12, some different). This influx was unusual, involving mostly adults. Of the remaining 20 autumn birds, 17 have been juveniles.

Black-headed Gull *Larus ridibundus*

Winter visitor and passage-migrant; common, locally abundant. Summer visitor; uncommon. Has bred.

Described in the last century as an abundant winter visitor, especially to the coast. It remains very common, and has increased inland, as in the rest of Britain, by virtue of its ability to exploit various modern human activities. Examples include the species' liking for rubbish dumps, and its ability to forage in most types of farmland. The overall increase has probably been partially offset by local declines on the levels, where drainage has reduced flooding. Wintering and autumn-passage birds arrive from mid-June and occur in substantial numbers by late July. Arrivals and passage continue, with the main arrival of wintering birds in November/December. Ringing recoveries indicate that the late summer/early autumn arrivals come from

British colonies, while the main influx consists of birds from Scandinavia and eastern Europe. Maximum numbers are present from late November to early March. There is some evidence of hard-weather arrivals, including two in severe weather in February 1986 that had been dye-marked in Denmark the previous autumn. Wintering birds depart from early February to late March, others passing through until late May; first-year birds predominate after early April. A few observations of visible migration, mostly in the Vale of Taunton, where they are regularly noted moving north-east in spring, and south or south-west in early autumn, the maximum being 1000 north-east on 7 March 1980. A few first-year birds usually summer on the coast.

A wide variety of food sources are used. Almost all categories of farmland are visited. Unlike Common and Herring Gulls, Black-headed Gulls particularly favour the levels. Very large numbers occur during and after floods: an estimated 16,000 were at Wet Moor, King's Moor and Midelney, 24 December 1972. Some of these birds parasitise Lapwings, which are often abundant at the same time. Other good feeding areas include the coast, especially tidal mudflats (e.g. Steart), and rubbish tips, which can attract over 1000 birds. Numbers scavenging these and in towns increase in severe weather. Few large feeding flocks recorded in the east and the far west, but is common throughout the county in winter, with the exception of Exmoor.

Birds feeding in Somerset appear to use at least 12 night roosts (see map opposite). In addition to these roosts, Luxhay Reservoir was used by up to 2000 or more feeding in the Wellington area, until at least 1976, but apparently not recently. Sutton Bingham is an occasional roost for up to 3500 birds when it is iced over. All main fresh waters in the county are used as loafing and bathing sites, particularly by birds en route to roosts.

They may have bred on the wetter levels before 1800. Several pairs bred on West Moor or Kingsbury Moor in 1942, 1944 and 1945, and two pairs bred at Muchelney in 1952. More recently, up to 2200 were on Wet Moor during floods in June 1979, at least 30 pairs attempting to breed, none successfully. One pair nested on Steart Island in 1983, and a pair were present at Porlock Marsh in late May 1974.

Ring-billed Gull *Larus delawarensis*

Vagrant.

Not noted in Britain until 1973; records have increased remarkably in recent years. To some extent this increase has been reflected in Somerset, where there have been eight birds at Sutton Bingham Reservoir since 1982. The

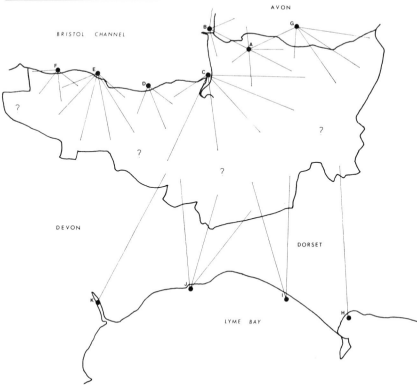

Black-headed Gull roosts: the lines on the map join known feeding areas and roosts, and are not intended to signify known flight lines. Of course, the use of some roosts are dependent on such variables as weather and tidal conditions.

A Cheddar Reservoir:	few counts; mid-winter average about 5000; 25,000, 31 January 1984, attracted by nearby flooded levels.
B Axe Estuary:	2500 to 4000.
C Parrett Estuary:	few counts, the only recent representative one being 17,000, 29 December 1986.
D Doniford:	small roost; no recent counts.
E Dunster Beach:	1000 to 1800.
F Porlock Marsh:	small roost, no counts.
G Chew Valley Lake (Avon)	each used by variable numbers of Somerset birds; several thousand fly to Chew, whereas very few go to the Exe. Some of those in the far west may go the Taw/ Torridge Estuary in north Devon.
H Weymouth Bay (Dorset)	
I West Bexington (Dorset)	
J Seaton Bay (Devon)	
K Exe Estuary (Devon)	

lack of records from other areas is surprising: the species is undoubtedly overlooked (but see Appendix). Just across the Bristol Channel is Blackpill, Swansea, which was the first site for Ring-billed Gulls and for some years the most regular .

The Sutton Bingham records are all of single birds: adults on 23 March 1982, 6 March 1983, 14 March 1984, 18/19 December 1985 and 20 March 1986; first-winter birds on 31 January 1982 and 21 October 1983; and a second-winter on 13 January 1985. Thus, half the records are in March, typical of the national pattern, which indicates a marked spring passage.

Common Gull   *Larus canus*

Winter visitor and passage-migrant; common, but local.

A reasonably numerous visitor to coastal and inland areas, and has probably been common locally inland for longer than the Black-headed Gull. Although it may be encountered anywhere in winter, large numbers occur less widely than Black-headed, due to the Common Gull's less catholic feeding preferences. The favourite foraging habitat is hill pasture, so the largest numbers are found on the Mendips, the lower hills south to Milborne Port, and on the Brendon Hills; flocks of 500 or more are not unusual. Elsewhere, apart from roosts (see below) much smaller numbers are general, though loafing flocks occur on the coast usually near roosts, and all the major reservoirs are used for loafing and bathing *en route* to and from roosts. Few scavenge around towns and at rubbish dumps, though these are used more in severe weather. Relatively few feed on the coast, and they are particularly scarce in the Vale of Taunton and on the levels, even during flooding. An outstanding exception to this is a record of 5000 on Westbury and Stoke Moors on 2 January 1986.

Common Gulls feeding in Somerset use at least six night roosts, but information is far from complete (see map).

Those feeding in extreme south-east Somerset may roost either at Weymouth Bay or Wareham Channel (Dorset). Up to 1300 have used Sutton Bingham *en route* to their roost, and up to 300 roost there when it is iced over.

The first birds begin to reappear from late June. Numbers remain small until October, though moderate flocks of passage birds sometimes occur on the coast from August. The main arrivals and passage are from mid-October. Virtually all counts over 100 are between October and March, with 94 per

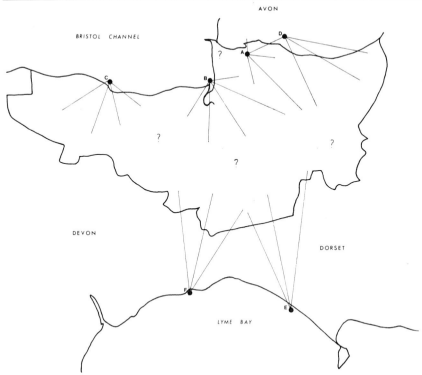

A Cheddar Reservoir: no regular counts, but up to 3000 in
                             December/January.
B Parrett Estuary: 1600 in 1955/56; recent incomplete
                             counts of 400.
C Dunster Beach: 1000 to 3000.
D Chew Valley Lake (Avon): counts there of 25,000, many of
                             which are birds from the Mendips.
E West Bexington (Dorset): used by up to 1300 or even more.
F Seaton Bay (Devon):   small numbers of Somerset birds
                             roost here.

cent of counts over 500 between November and February. Three ringing
recoveries (one October, two January) all of Norwegian birds. Wintering
birds depart from February to early April, others passing until mid-May;
mostly first-year birds after early April. Movements are occasionally
observed, mostly on the coast, as on three dates between 8 and 17 March
1972, when 133 flew north off Brean Down. Rare between mid-May and late
June.

Lesser Black-backed Gull   *Larus fuscus*

British race *L.f. graellsii*
Resident (or summer visitor); decreased. Passage-migrant and winter visitor; locally common and increasing.

First recorded breeding in World War II, when a mixed colony with Herring Gulls was established on Steart Island. First estimated at 40 pairs in 1946, numbers remained stable for some time but then there was an increase, with 171 nests counted in 1969. The last count was 30 pairs in 1976, but the colony has subsequently disappeared, possibly as a result of fox predation. There are isolated breeding records from the River Brue at Westhay, and from Luxhay Reservoir, and birds now regularly summer in Taunton and Yeovil, where up to three pairs have nested on roofs, following the example of Herring Gulls.

Increasing as passage and winter visitor for 20 years or more. Spring passage is protracted, with migrants noted widely from mid-February to late May, and a poorly-marked peak between late March and early May. The largest movement recorded is 100 or more moving east off Bossington on 11 April 1967. Inland, migration is regularly observed in the Vale of Taunton (up to 90 flying north-east per spring), and at Sutton Bingham Reservoir. Increases are also noted in other areas, such as Cheddar Reservoir, where several hundred may be present in early spring, and on the levels.

In May and June continues to occur in moderate numbers on the levels, with a few elsewhere. Though some of these are late migrants most are probably foraging birds from the breeding colony on Steep Holm (Avon). The numbers involved can be substantial: in June 1979 flocks of 250 and 100 were seen at two places on the levels feeding on dead fish after an exceptional summer flood; these were probably birds that would normally have been scattered over a wider area, feeding in pasture and along the rivers. Flocks have been observed returning westwards over the levels to Steep Holm on summer evenings. A few immature birds also summer. One record of 150 first-summer birds in late May at the Axe Estuary suggests a tendency for immatures to summer close to the Steep Holm colony.

From mid-July birds begin to appear more widely again, migrating along the coast and inland through the Vale of Taunton, over Sutton Bingham Reservoir and elsewhere. Such movements continue erratically until November. For example, at Sutton Bingham, peak movements of up to 100 have occurred in August, October and November, often on days preceding or following others when very few are recorded. From August, large gatherings begin to appear in the north and east, feeding more on ploughed land than pasture, and flying to roost at Chew Valley Lake (Avon). An exceptional influx involved up to 1000 at Wells in late August/early September 1986. Some autumn birds are no doubt birds dispersing from Steep Holm, but records of the race *L.f. intermedius* suggest that many are migrants from further afield. By late November, numerous only in the east and north, where sizeable flocks are found on pasture and at rubbish tips, these still roosting at Chew Valley Lake. Elsewhere, small numbers occur in winter, mostly on the levels and coast, but they are particularly scarce in west Somerset. There are small winter roosts at Steart (recent maximum 23), Dunster Beach (up to 20) and Cheddar Reservoir (maximum of 38). A few roosted at Luxhay Reservoir until the mid-1970s. Adults form the vast majority of the winter population; immatures, which winter further south, are most numerous in autumn. Movements have been noted in response to hard weather.

This species' movements and distribution are thus seen to be complex and erratic.

North European race *L.f. intermedius*
Passage-migrant; scarce.

North Scandinavian race *L.f. fuscus*
Vagrant.

Although named in 1922, *intermedius* was largely ignored until recently. It breeds in Denmark, Holland and southern Norway, and is far more likely to occur than *fuscus*, which breeds in northern Scandinavia and migrates south overland. About 60 *fuscus* were recorded up to 1982 (including a flock of about 30 flying off Glenthorne in late March 1956 or 1957). Mainly on the coast, and at reservoirs and elsewhere inland, between October and April.

It is likely that most if not all of the old records were of *intermedius*, which is now regularly reported between August and April, but mostly from November to February; usually ones or twos, but an exceptional count of 35 at Cheddar Reservoir, 10 January 1985.

There are two recent records of birds showing characteristics of *fuscus*: an adult at Hinkley Point, 18 February 1986, and one at Cheddar Reservoir, 13 February 1987.

Iceland Gull *Larus glaucoides*

Vagrant.

Twelve records of single birds, first- or second-years except where stated:
Somerton, not aged, 12 December 1881; Brean Down, not aged, 20 May
1930; Cheddar Reservoir, 19 April 1939, 2 January 1973, 25–29 September
1973, and 20 March 1974, the latter three probably attracted to the nearby
rubbish tip; Dunster Beach, 26–28 January 1957; Steart, 10–24 March,
20–27 April and 19 October 1974; Sutton Bingham Reservoir, adults, 19
January 1983 and 4 January 1985; Hinkley Point, 25 March 1988.

Glaucous Gull *Larus hyperboreus*

Vagrant.

At least ten records of single birds since 1951. All are first-year birds except
where stated. About eight on the coast from the Axe Estuary to Hinkley
Point: 11 February 1951 (age not given); 1 May 1976 (also a white-winged
gull, possibly this bird, 25 May); different birds 10 and 20 December 1982;
probably one bird, 6 January, 26 February and 6 March 1983; 10 January
1984; a second-summer, 29 April and 10 May 1987; 19 April 1988.
Elsewhere, a second-winter bird at Minehead, 24–30 December 1968; one,
Sutton Bingham Reservoir, 28 January 1984.

In addition to these, a second-winter Glaucous Gull at Hinkley Point, 12
February–9 April 1985, showed slight hybrid characteristics, and a first-
winter bird at Sutton Bingham Reservoir, 23 January 1985, was thought to
be a hybrid Glaucous X Herring Gull.

Herring Gull *Larus argentatus*

North-western European race *L.a. argenteus*
*Resident, passage-migrant and winter visitor. Common, but
decreased.*

Little known of breeding status before 1900. A colony was established on
Steart Island during World War II; first estimated at 100 pairs in 1946, then

increased rapidly. In 1969, 3121 nests were counted, but numbers were halved by 1976, and shortly after this the colony became extinct, probably due to fox predation. Until about 1968, 200 pairs nested along the Stolford to Glenthorne coast, mostly west of Minehead. Since then the breeding numbers have declined to only about 80 coastal pairs despite the establishment of a new colony of up to 21 pairs at Hinkley Point Power Station. Small numbers have bred occasionally at Steart Point and at Brean. Reasons for the decline, especially in the west, are unknown. Coinciding with this decline was the colonization of roofs in five inland areas. However, due to the noise and debris they create, the gulls have been persecuted at all five sites, their nest and eggs being destroyed. The total population of these colonies has fallen from a peak of at least 250 pairs in 1981 to under 100 in 1986. The colonies (with year when first noted breeding in brackets), and highest estimates are as follows: Westland's Factory, Yeovil (1973), at least ten pairs in 1983; Burnham-on-Sea (1975), 87 nests destroyed in 1981; Bridgwater (1976), 110 nests destroyed but many others successful in 1981; Wellington (1977), 80 eggs destroyed in 1981, indicating around 30 nests; Taunton town centre (1978), 20 or more pairs in 1983.

Widespread as a non-breeding bird but it appears to have decreased and has certainly changed its habits. Some of the autumn and winter population originates from the Steep Holm colony (Avon), and formerly came from the Steart Island colony. However, the winter population is augmented by arrivals from further afield, as indicated from the occasional bird of the Scandinavian race *argentatus*.

Inland, most abundant in winter. Few migratory movements have been recorded, but 300 flew north-east at Porlock Bay on 11 April 1966, and 150 flew west in 15 minutes in mid-channel off Minehead, 27 December 1966. Also occurs regularly elsewhere at passage times, in areas like Norton St Philip.

Until recently, foraged in substantial numbers on farmland, including the levels (particularly when flooded); permanent pasture was favoured, with earthworms the main food source. Large numbers also fed in intertidal areas, at sewage outflows and rubbish dumps. Few counts available, perhaps because the species was so ubiquitous that it was virtually ignored. However, up to 3000 were noted at Minehead in autumn in 1954 and 1968, mainly at the sewage outfall.

During the 1970s there was a major change in habits; although Herring Gulls are still very widespread, large numbers are now restricted mainly to rubbish dumps, some of which have closed in recent years. In 1972 and 1973 up to 10,000 occurred at Cheddar Reservoir, but much smaller numbers here since the closure of Axbridge tip in the mid-1970s. Hundreds feed at tips at Poole, Bathpool and Treborough; the recent closure of Yeovil tip resulted in much lower numbers in the Yeovil/Sutton Bingham Reservoir area. Now relatively scarce on farmland, especially on the levels, and even on the coast west of Stolford, where its numbers have greatly declined.

Only one night roost is known in the county, at Steart Island, but there are no winter counts from here. Luxhay Reservoir, where 1000 or more roosted till the mid-1970s, is no longer used. Birds in the north-east roost at Chew Valley Lake; those in the Yeovil area roost on the Dorset coast; west coast birds fly to Lynmouth; and those from the south-west go to the Axe, Exe and Taw/Torridge (all Devon). Most fresh waters are used for bathing prior to roost flights, though to a lesser extent than by other gulls.

Scandinavian race *L.a. argentatus*
Vagrant, but possibly regular winter visitor.

Only three records: adults at Sutton Bingham Reservoir, 24 January 1985 and 18/19 February 1986, and a third-winter at Cheddar Reservoir, 31 December 1987. This race is evidently overlooked, for it is common in winter in some parts of Britain.

Mediterranean race *L.a. michahellis*
Passage-migrant and winter visitor; rare.

This yellow-legged race, considerd by some authorities to be a separate species, has increased in Britain in recent years, following its northward expansion in France. There are 17 Somerset records involving at least 14 birds, all since 1982. These have been at Sutton Bingham Reservoir (at least six), Cheddar Reservoir (five or six), Wells (two), and Hinkley Point (one). Five were from July to October, one in November, the rest December to March. The total includes eight adults and three juveniles.

Great Black-backed Gull *Larus marinus*

Resident; decreased. Passage-migrant and winter visitor; locally fairly common.

Bred fairly regularly on Steart Island, 1956–76, with a maximum of 17 pairs in 1969, but has bred there in only two years since. Elsewhere, one pair bred at Ivystone (Culbone) in 1968, and breeding suspected around Hurlstone Point, where regular in spring and summer; two pairs breed regularly just across the border in Devon.

As a non-breeding visitor, occurs in small numbers along the whole coast, but from the Axe Estuary to Hinkley Point is most numerous in autumn and winter; counts of up to 30 mainly in September/October, probably from the Steep Holm colony. Some remain to winter, perhaps augmented by arrivals from further north; up to 36 have recently been counted at Hinkley Point. From here to the Devon border there is also an autumn and winter peak of up to 25, but some birds are present in small numbers throughout the year, feeding along the shore or in offshore waters. There is apparently a night roost at Steep Holm although no counts have been made, and up to 15 have roosted at Dunster Beach.

There is no detectable spring passage along the coast, and those present at this time and in summer are probably from Steep Holm.

Inland, has increased in recent decades, and now frequent in very small numbers, especially at the reservoirs and over the levels. Birds occasionally forage in pasture or scavenge at rubbish tips, but most of these appear to be transient. Recorded in all months, but most from December until March, with a peak in the latter month, indicating a definite spring passage. For example, 16 flew north at Sutton Bingham Reservoir from 5 to 23 March 1984. Inland records are usually of one to five birds; the maximum is 20 at Cheddar Reservoir, 20 April 1968; there are few records from the east or west. There is also evidence of a slight autumn passage.

Kittiwake *Rissa tridactyla*

Passage-migrant, summer and winter visitor; local.

Scarce until the mid 1960s, but now much increased due to more sea-watching and to the establishment since 1970 of a colony of up to 500 pairs in the Woody Bay area 10km west of the Somerset border. Older records usually refer to 'wrecks' in which many of the birds died. The largest of these was in mid-February 1957, when 101 occurred, 70 of them inland, including 50 at Cheddar Reservoir.

Coastal movements are now regular, often coinciding with strong winds: typically, westerlies push birds up the Bristol Channel and against the Brean to Steart coast; winds then moderate and veer north-west, allowing the Kittiwakes to retreat westwards along the coast from Watchet to Porlock. Also noted more frequently inland in recent years too.

In August seen quite frequently in very small numbers along the entire coast, presumably as birds disperse from breeding colonies further west. There are also nine inland records, mostly single birds at Cheddar Reservoir. Fewer remain off the coast in September/October, when they are very rare inland.

From November they become more numerous; sizeable movements can occur throughout the winter, though December has seen the largest numbers, particularly off the Watchet to Porlock coast. The maxima here are 4000–5000, 21 December 1982, in a strong north-west wind, and 'probably several thousand' west, 24 December 1984. Off Berrow, 1592 flew south in only 50 minutes, 11 December 1983. Records are fewer in February, though large movements still may occur. From November to February, appears inland quite regularly, with 30 records, mostly of single birds, at Cheddar and Sutton Bingham Reservoirs; an exception was 33 flying south at Sutton Bingham, 23 December 1982, shortly after one of the large coastal movements mentioned above.

Becomes more frequent in March, with quite regular movements late in the month continuing through April into May, mainly off the Brean Down to Steart coast. These probably involve both passage-migrants and parties of feeding birds from colonies further west. Regular watching from Brean Down has shown movements tend to be up-channel early in the day, with return movements late. Spring maxima off Brean Down: 380 north, 23 March 1972; 260 north, 29 April 1981; 166, 12 May 1978. Spring produces the largest inland numbers. Over 20 records between March and early May, with three large movements: 80, Cheddar Reservoir, 26 April 1981 (part of a national influx during snow and strong north-east winds); at least 114, Sutton Bingham Reservoir, 28 April 1985; 35, over Westhay Moor, 25 March 1986.

In June and July, scarce off the Brean Down to Steart coast, but remains regular in small numbers further west (probably the Devon breeding birds).

Adults usually outnumber first-year birds by ten or more to one. However, in August the proportion of juveniles is high, slowly decreasing till late autumn.

Ivory Gull   *Pagophila eburnea*

Vagrant.

One very old record: adult shot, Bridgwater, about 1819 (Woodforde Collection).

Caspian Tern   *Sterna caspia*

Vagrant.

One record: an adult, Durleigh Reservoir, 16 July 1977, with presumably the same bird at Steart Point later the same day.

Sandwich Tern   *Sterna sandvicensis*

Passage-migrant; scarce and local.

First recorded in 1923. From then until 1965 about 185 were seen, and there have been over 600 since; they seem to have become rather more frequent, but this may be a reflection of more intensive sea- and reservoir-watching. They occur mostly along the coast, in Bridgwater Bay and in the west, but about 15 per cent have been inland, almost all at Cheddar and Sutton Bingham Reservoirs; a few records from other waters and from an inland flight-line along the Vale of Taunton Deane.

About 20 per cent of all records have been in spring, from 7 April to May, with a peak in mid-April; only seven inland. A further 10 per cent have been in June and are probably wandering non-breeders. Autumn passage from July to late October, the peak period being 1–10 September. The highest spring count is of a total of 22 on the Minehead/Porlock shore, 12 April 1966, and the highest in autumn is 56 at Dunster Beach, 20 August 1983. Only two records after October, the later being of one at Cheddar Reservoir, 6 December 1945.

A juvenile colour-ringed on the Farne Is. (Northumberland) was seen at Sutton Bingham Reservoir, 12 October 1985.

Roseate Tern   *Sterna dougallii*

Vagrant.

There are six records of the rarest of Britain's breeding terns, all of single birds: Cheddar Reservoir, 5–7 May 1954; an adult, Durleigh Reservoir, 5 September 1967; an adult, Cheddar Reservoir, 29 September 1968; Steart, 6 May 1973; Berrow Golf Course, 10/11 June 1979; Sutton Bingham Reservoir, 10 June 1984.

Common Tern   *Sterna hirundo*
Arctic Tern   *Sterna paradisaea*

Passage-migrants; local.

These species are hard to separate and, although identification criteria are now better established, many birds cannot safely be assigned to a species, especially on distant coastal views. So we have to treat them together.

Reported as passage-migrants since records began in the mid-nineteenth century, usually in small numbers, but with occasional irruptions after spring gales. Among older records, such influxes were noted in May 1842 and April 1947.

Since 1966, over 10,000 have been seen. About 75 per cent of all these have been spring birds in Bridgwater Bay; dates range from 4 April to 20 June; few occur before 20 April, and the peak period is 1–10 May. The remaining 25 per cent have mostly been at Cheddar Reservoir, with others on small waters and on the western coast. Higher spring counts have often coincided with winds between north and east, or with strong westerlies.

In spring 1974, a total of 1700 were seen, including 600 flying north off Brean Down and 490 off Berrow on 27 April, and 100 at Cheddar Reservoir on 3 May, which is the highest inland count. In spring 1984 there were 1500, including 392 to the north off Burnham-on-Sea on 1 May; most were Arctics, including 84 at Sutton Bingham Reservoir, also on 1 May. The influx of 1947 was also mainly of Arctics, which may predominate among windblown birds in spring. The peak dates before 1966 seem to have been rather later than in recent years.

In the same period, autumn migration has been recorded from late June to 13 November; the total number of birds each year has been between 35 and

360, less variable than in spring. Most occur from 14 August to 20 September, with two apparent peaks: 10–20 August and 1–10 September. There are a few November records of single birds, and even two in December, the latest being an Arctic at Cheddar Reservoir, 12 December 1949. Most occur at the major reservoirs, in Bridgwater Bay (where they are less numerous than in spring) and on western coasts (where they are more common). The remainder are on smaller waters or on overland flights, but there are only two records for east Somerset. The highest autumn counts usually coincide with strong winds between south-west and north-west, which displace Irish Sea migrants: there have been eight counts between 50 and 100 on the coast from Dunster to Porlock Bay, and there were 75 at Cheddar Reservoir, 5 September 1967.

Before 1966, only about 10 per cent were specifically identified, and the overall figure since then is no better, although it has improved in very recent years. Figures are distorted by the spring irruptions, but in most recent years numbers of identified Commons and Arctics in spring have been about equal, or there have been slightly more Arctics, whereas in autumn Commons have had the advantage by up to ten to one. Arctics tend to come later in the autumn, with most from September to mid-October.

Forster's Tern *Sterna forsteri*

Vagrant.

One record of this North American species, which has only recently been found to visit Britain: Hinkley Point, 7–12 February 1987. Winter records are typical of British sightings.

Little Tern *Sterna albifrons*

Passage-migrant; scarce and local. Formerly bred.

This is the only tern known to have bred in Somerset. On Steart Island, one pair bred in 1924, four pairs in 1925 (and several others on Steart Island), two in 1926, and one in 1928 and 1930; birds may also have bred in 1923 and 1927.

Few nineteenth-century records. Slightly more were recorded on passage from 1925 to 1965 than from 1966 to 1986, so it would seem that they are a good deal scarcer today, as would be expected, as they have proved so vulnerable to disturbance on breeding beaches.

About 20 per cent of these have been in spring, from 11 April to 9 June, with a peak in the first half of May. Autumn dates range from July to 25 October, but 80 per cent have been between 1 August and 10 September; the peak period has been a little later in very recent years. They occur mostly along the coast of Bridgwater Bay and in the west, with others inland, especially at Cheddar and Durleigh Reservoirs. Apparently once more common than today in the west in spring, but such comparisons probably reflect the distribution of observers. The highest counts have been: in spring, 14, Parrett Estuary, 14 May 1960; in autumn, 25, Minehead, 20 August 1948. No recent counts have exceeded five in spring or 12 in autumn, but mention should be made of an exceptional 11 at Sutton Bingham Reservoir, 20 August 1983. Some records coincide with strong winds.

Whiskered Tern   *Chlidonias hybridus*

Vagrant.

Three records of single birds: Durleigh Reservoir, 13/14 May 1973 (also seen at Chilton Trinity on the latter date); an adult in almost complete summer plumage, Cheddar Reservoir, 23 September–4 October 1976; Sutton Bingham Reservoir, 29 May 1983.

Black Tern   *Chlidonias niger*

Passage-migrant; local and scarce.

May have bred on the levels before 1800. Since records began in the mid-nineteenth century there is little evidence that its total numbers as a passage-migrant have greatly changed, though in the last 20 years it has been much more common in autumn than in spring.

Numbers are very variable at both seasons. Birds often appear when the winds are between north-east and south-east, and in autumn sometimes in westerlies. Of the 2000 seen since 1965, only about 25 per cent have been in spring. These pass from 8 April to 10 June, but mostly in early June. Annual totals range from none to over 100. Most are at Cheddar Reservoir, or on the coast of Bridgwater Bay, with some at other waters. Rare on the levels, but the latest record in spring, of four over floods on Wet Moor, 10 June 1979, was a reminder of the past. The highest spring count has been 75, at Cheddar Reservoir, 12 May 1949.

The much greater autumn passage lasts from late June to November, but is also very variable, with recent annual totals of between 25 and 200. The peak period for any one autumn may be as late as October (as in 1981), but 90 per cent pass in August and September. Over 40 per cent of all these have been at Cheddar Reservoir, with the rest mainly in Bridgwater Bay and at Durleigh and Sutton Bingham Reservoirs. Others have been off the western coast or on smaller waters. The highest autumn count was of 400 at Durleigh and the Parrett Estuary, September 1957, but in recent years the most seen together has been about 70 at Cheddar, 20 September 1980. The latest record is of a remarkable flock of 29 at Steart Island, 24 November 1980.

White-winged Black Tern   *Chlidonias leucopterus*

Vagrant.

After its first appearance in Somerset in 1968, there were records for seven of the next nine years. There have now been records of 12 birds, seven juveniles and the others winter-plumaged birds. Four have been at Cheddar Reservoir, three at Sutton Bingham, two each at Durleigh and the Parrett Estuary and one on King's Moor. Once in spring (adult, Durleigh, 29–31 May 1970), and the rest in autumn from 12 August to 9 October; usually with Black Terns, and often after south-easterly winds.

Guillemot   *Uria aalge*

Non-breeding summer visitor, passage-migrant and storm-vagrant; scarce and local.

Earlier records are scanty, but until recently Guillemots seem to have been less common than Razorbills. They have occurred fairly regularly in the Channel, especially the western end, since at least the 1920s. Most are seen from May to July, though there are records of live birds in all months except March. The nearest colony is around Woody Bay in North Devon, where 549 birds were counted in 1987, the most since regular records started in 1952. The increase in this colony must account for the larger number of records since 1965, which at 120 are almost as many as those of Razorbills. Usually in ones or twos, but small parties of up to 11 have been seen, mainly off the Porlock–Glenthorne coast in summer. Very recent observations suggest that Guillemots may be under-recorded, especially in winter: on 21 December 1985, 90 unidentified auks flew west in Minehead Bay, with five definite Guillemots.

Casualties, often oiled, are two or three times as numerous as those of Razorbills. Since 1965, 26 have been found, of which 11 have been on the east coast of Bridgwater Bay. Most have been from September to February, often after strong westerlies, when living birds are also numerous. Out of 49 casualties between 1912 and 1965, 15 were assigned to the darker Northern race, *U.a. aalge*; these were all between 15 September and 28 April.

Razorbill   *Alca torda*

Non-breeding summer visitor, passage-migrant, and storm-vagrant; scarce and local.

Before 1900, apparently more common than other auks in the Channel, but reliable evidence is scarce, and even now a lot of auks go unidentified offshore. Since the 1920s, its status has differed little from the Guillemot's; there have been slightly more records, especially in April. Observed in all months, though mainly in summer and in October. The North Devon colony around Woody Bay held 406 birds in 1987; as with the Guillemot, this is the highest total since records began in 1952. More common off western coasts, but about 30 per cent of all birds have been seen in Bridgwater Bay or off Brean Down. Very small numbers are usual, but on 30 July 1977 about 30 were seen from a boat well offshore.

From 1925 to 1965, about 26 were found dead or exhausted on the coast, so it is perhaps surprising that there have been only nine such records since; recent casualties have been from February to May, and in October and November. There have only ever been two inland records, from Cothelstone and Durleigh Reservoir.

To these records of the two larger auks must be added a total of around 120 unidentified birds since 1965; 80 per cent of these have been in the Channel west of Watchet, and most in April, May or October.

Black Guillemot *Cepphus grylle*

Vagrant.

Two records: one off St.Audries 'before 1869'; four flying west off Dunster Beach, 7 February 1954.

Little Auk *Alle alle*

Winter visitor or storm-vagrant; rare.

First recorded in 1805. About 54 have occurred since 1863; of these only 15 since 1965, including two in February 1988. The total is swelled by the 22 involved in a wreck around Burnham-on-Sea, 9–12 February 1950. Most have been storm casualties, in recent years mainly from mid-November to late February, though there are older records for August–October and March. About 22 have been found inland in a variety of places all over the county, the remainder along the coast, especially the east shore of Bridgwater Bay. This is exposed to the westerlies that displace a pelagic but vulnerable species.

Puffin *Fratercula arctica*

Winter visitor and storm-vagrant; very rare.

There were occasional coastal records in the last century, and three inland casualties, 1878/88. Since 1922 there have been only eight records of healthy birds, all but two off the western coast between July and October. They include a party of 12 off Minehead, 10 August 1951. The odd two records were in the Parrett Estuary, in November and January.

Since 1915 there have been about 23 casualties, mostly from October to February on the coast; they are usually victims of gales. None has been driven inland since one appeared at Cheddar Reservoir on 4 November 1967, but there were earlier records for six places in central and south Somerset.

Pallas's Sandgrouse   *Syrrhaptes paradoxus*

Vagrant.

Two were shot near Huntspill in 1872. In the great invasion of 1888, about 40 were seen or shot from 25 May to July, including 20 near Norton St Philip and 11 on Steart Island, with others at Burnham-on-Sea, Charlinch and Nynehead.

Feral Pigeon (Rock Dove)   *Columba livia*

Resident; presumably common.

There is no evidence to suggest that the Rock Dove has ever occurred in a truly wild state. Its descendant the Feral Pigeon is almost completely ignored by ornithologists, and very little has been published about its distribution within the county. The *Breeding Atlas* confirmed breeding in 11 of the county's 10-km squares, with probable or possible breeding in a further five. This reflects the distribution of observers rather than that of the species.

A colony of up to 400 exists at Burnham-on-Sea, and a smaller one at Berrow, both centred on the churches; there must be similar colonies in many towns, for instance Bridgwater and Taunton, or on cliffs within the county. Has bred on the cliffs at Brean Down, but possibly not for about 20 years. Previously bred in Cheddar Gorge, where it probably still does so, and on the cliffs between Blue Anchor and Watchet.

Stock Dove   *Columba oenas*

Resident, winter visitor and probably passage-migrant; locally fairly common.

Before 1865, a rare winter visitor; now a reasonably common resident, and a winter visitor in variable numbers. Also occurs in small numbers during cold weather, moving south or south-west with other species.

It was certainly breeding by 1873 and by 1900 was thinly distributed over most of the county where old timber provided suitable nest-sites. At that time the central parts were considered the most favoured, and that probably holds true today. However, it was thought to have decreased during the 1960s, because of felling of old elm trees. Breeding is not confined to trees; several colonies exist on the cliffs of Brean Down and Cheddar Gorge, and on the cliffs in the west. On Exmoor they more often nest in cattle sheds, barns and deserted buildings than in trees. The *Breeding Atlas* confirmed breeding in 23 of the county's 10-km squares, with probable or possible breeding in a further nine; has apparently increased since then.

Winter flocks of up to 200 are reasonably frequent, but up to 400 are not unknown in the Parrett Estuary, and at Witcombe Bottom, where by far the highest total recorded in the county occurred on 29 November 1983, when about 1100 were feeding on a ploughed field.

Woodpigeon   *Columba palumbus*

Resident, passage-migrant and winter visitor; common.

A widely distributed resident, and very common. The *Breeding Atlas* proved breeding in all the county's 10-km squares. A regular passage-migrant in small numbers, mainly in October and November, and a winter visitor in variable numbers depending on the severity of the weather. Cold-weather movements to the south or south-west occur during such times. In winter, flocks are widespread on stubble fields and on the levels; usually under 1000, but on occasions up to 2000 are recorded.

Collared Dove   *Streptopelia decaocto*

Resident and passage-migrant; fairly common.

The first county record was of one at Minehead on 18 May 1963, followed by pairs at Bridgwater, Pawlett and Porlock. By 1964 it had become established, mainly on the coast, but it had also reached inland as far as Cheddar and Nettlecombe. The following year it had reached the east and the south of the county.

The *Breeding Atlas* confirmed breeding in 26 of the county's 10-km squares with probable or possible breeding in a further three. Since then it has increased and spread over the greater part of the county; however, during the past decade some observers have thought that the population had stabilised or even decreased, at least in some parts. Collared Doves have

become a regular feature around grain mills and as such have suffered severe control at some sites. Wintering flocks are generally small, up to 30, but on occasions up to 150 are noted.

In most years, birds are observed flying south along the coast at Berrow, usually in April or May. Similar movements have been noted at Brean Down, but here the movements are complicated, with birds flying in various directions, including west. Smaller numbers are recorded in autumn, usually from August to October. These movements seem to be confined to the coastal strip, but may be overlooked elsewhere. Has occurred on Steep Holm, but with such confused movement recorded, much is still to be learnt of the origin and destination of these migrants.

Turtle Dove   *Streptopelia turtur*

Summer visitor; very local. Passage-migrant; scarce. Decreasing.

There are few published details of distribution, but probably it is very thinly distributed on the lower ground wherever suitable woods and tall hedgerows afford nesting sites. Most frequently found in the central and southern parts, and is decidedly scarce in the west; probably never really a common bird anywhere in the county, at least during the present century.

The *Breeding Atlas* confirmed breeding in 14 of the county's 10-km squares, with probable or possible breeding in a further 12. A decline was first noted in 1977 and this has continued, bringing the present population to possibly as few as 20 pairs. Information on its status is particularly scarce for the 1960s and early 1970s, so the drastic decline may have been going on for several decades. The cause is uncertain, but is probably due to a combination of a number of factors: persecution on migration in the Mediterranean countries, where it is a prime target for so-called sportsmen; the deterioration of the weather in the Sahel; and even perhaps our own rather cool, wet summers in recent years.

Recorded between 12 April and 16 October, with the breeding birds usually arriving from late April and leaving by the end of August. As a passage-migrant, it is now infrequent, and then in only small numbers. However, unprecedented passage was recorded at Cheddar Reservoir on 24 May 1977, when 63 flew north-east in one and a half hours.

Ring-necked Parakeet   *Psittacula krameri*

Vagrant.

Only four records, all single birds, of a species afforded 'Category D' status: Durleigh Reservoir, 20 and 23 January 1980; Yeovil, 4 August 1985; Ember Combe, 9 August 1985; Berrow, several dates between 16 July and 28 February 1988 – this bird commuted between there and the Brean Down Bird Gardens, where it was identified as belonging to one of the Indian races, probably *P.k. borealis*.

Most, if not all, are likely to be escapes, rather than feral birds.

Cuckoo   *Cuculus canorus*

Summer visitor and passage-migrant; fairly common and wide-spread.

Generally distributed throughout the county, but there are few reports from the east, probably due to lack of observers rather than of birds. Usually

arrives from mid-April (earliest, 25 March 1943) and leaves July/August. There are a few records for September and October, but the latest bird recorded was at Hatch Beauchamp on 12 November 1958. There are many conflicting reports concerning the numbers of birds present each year, but perhaps they fluctuate in different parts of the county. The Cuckoo can be found almost anywhere from sea level to the highest ground; in particular, the peat-moors, the levels and Exmoor are favoured, with Meadow Pipits the main host on the latter. The *Breeding Atlas* confirmed breeding in 20 of the county's 10-km squares, with probable or possible breeding in a further 17.

Yellow-billed Cuckoo *Coccyzus americanus*

Vagrant.

One record: a female shot at Pylle, 6 October 1901.

Barn Owl *Tyto alba*

Resident; local and scarce. Declining.

Heavily persecuted before 1914; Taunton taxidermists apparently used to receive about 50 a year. Wide fluctuations were reported in the 1920s and 1930s, and again in the 1950s. It disappeared from parts of north Exmoor

about 1950, but evidently increased in central Somerset between 1945 and 1955. Since then there has been a steady decline, which is still continuing. Modern farming methods, including the use of pesticides, loss of traditional nest-sites and habitat, in addition to continued persecution and disturbance, have all contributed to the present low level of population. The number of birds found dead on roadsides is particularly depressing. However, the provision of nestboxes in some modern barns has yielded results.

Widely but thinly distributed. Probably most numerous on the peat-moors and levels; the number of reported pairs in any one year varies from one to ten. Occasionally pairs are present at sites but do not breed, perhaps due to a shortage of prey or even to inexperience. The *Breeding Atlas* confirmed breeding in 19 of the county's 10-km squares, with probable or possible breeding in a further three.

Snowy Owl *Nyctea scandiaca*

Vagrant.

At least four records, all of single birds on Exmoor: 22 March 1876; various places between Haddon Hill and Dunster, 12 October 1925 to 15 March 1926; Haddon Hill, 18 January 1930; near Simonsbath, 26 January 1945.

Another, taken with a damaged wing in Cheddar Gorge, 15 September 1933, may have been an escape.

Little Owl *Athene noctua*

Resident; locally fairly common.

First reached Somerset in 1911 at Isle Abbotts; from there spread astonishingly fast to most parts by 1925.

The *Breeding Atlas* confirmed breeding in 22 of the county's 10-km squares, with probable or possible breeding in a further eight. Reasonably common over most agricultural land where there are suitable nest-sites, but remains rather scarce in the west. Recent reports suggest that the population has remained fairly steady, although some local decreases have been noted. Has suffered in some parts by the removal of elms; the cumulative effect of herbicides and pesticides remains to be seen.

Tawny Owl *Strix aluco*

Resident; common.

Heavily persecuted in the last century by gamekeepers, but never became really scarce. There is little information published on population trends, but it is apparently a common and widely distributed resident, particularly in more wooded parts. The *Breeding Atlas* confirmed breeding in 32 of the county's 10-km squares, with probable or possible breeding in a further two, making this the most widespread of the owls, and presumably the most common.

Long-eared Owl   *Asio otus*

Winter visitor; rare. Has bred.

Bred, or possibly bred, at several localities during the first 40 years of this century, but not recorded from 1942 until 1973, when one was heard calling from Stock Hill on 7 January. A pair reared two young there in 1974, the first breeding record for 32 years; no breeding records since, but two were present there on 29 May the following year. One in a garden at Watchet, 16 May 1987, was presumably a late migrant.

Apart from these, mainly a rare winter visitor, more numerous during cold-weather influxes from the Continent, but can easily be overlooked. Usually singly, occasionally in twos, but four in an ivy-covered tree in Taunton between 22 February and 14 March 1976 was most unusual.

What was presumed to be the same bird returned to roost at Helland Hill, near North Curry, in successive winters, 1982–85.

Short-eared Owl   *Asio flammeus*

Winter visitor and passage-migrant; uncommon. Has bred.

Primarily an uncommon winter visitor in fluctuating numbers, in some years almost common at some localities (21 at West Sedge Moor on 1 December 1950). Also a passage-migrant in small numbers, mostly in the autumn. Has arrived as early as 10 August, but the main arrival is not usually until after the middle of October. Usually leaves by March but there have been several records in April and May recently.

A pair bred on Exford Common in 1939, and a pair on the South Levels in 1979 may have bred. Other summer records include one over South

Petherton, 28 June 1949, two at different localities in 1972, and one at Rookham on 20 June 1976.

Has been recorded throughout the county from the coast to the high ground in the west, but few in the east. Prefers the rougher fields and moors, coastal *Spartina* and *Phragmites*, and heather moorland. The most favoured areas are the Parrett Estuary and West Sedge Moor, which between them may hold up to 20 in a good year.

Nightjar   *Caprimulgus europaeus*

Summer visitor; scarce and local, decreasing.

Its preferred habitat includes bracken-covered hillsides, young fir plantations, cleared woodland with regenerated undergrowth, and areas of birch scrub, but it has even bred on shingle at Porlock.

Decreases were first noted as early as 1880, and it has continued to decline. In 1957 described as 'relatively common', but only six years later 'local and scarce'. The 1981 BTO Survey gave us the most complete coverage in recent years. The results showed that Somerset may have held 45–50 pairs out of a possible national total of about 2100. The following year only 20–23 pairs were recorded, although admittedly the coverage was less complete, but numbers have dropped further since; in 1985 only 14 males were reported, with none at Shapwick Heath, once a stronghold regularly holding up to eight males. The following year showed a slight improvement, with 17 males located, including two at Shapwick.

It has been difficult to attribute the decline to any one factor. Several theories have been put forward: pesticides, destruction of habitat (probably a major factor in the decline on Shapwick Heath), and a combination of late arrival, cool wet summers, lack of insects, all contributing to poor breeding success and lack of second broods (Berry and Bibby, 1981).

The *Breeding Atlas* confirmed breeding in only six of the county's 10-km squares, with probable or possible breeding in a further seven. Recorded widely throughout the county, but only in small pockets where suitable habitat occurs. The main areas are the peat-moors, Quantocks, Blackdowns and Exmoor. There are no recent breeding records from the Mendips, but several pairs can still be found in the east of the county.

Swift *Apus apus*

Summer visitor and passage-migrant; common.

Widely distributed and common, breeding in towns, villages and isolated houses, but scarce on the high ground, where it is common only on feeding flights. Most nest under the eaves of houses, but in recent years one or two pairs have nested in House Martins' nests at Crewkerne. The *Breeding Atlas* confirmed breeding in 33 of the county's 10-km squares, with probable or possible breeding in a further four.

Usually arrives during the last week of April (earliest, 27 March 1897), but the main arrival is during the first ten days of May (consistently arrives suddenly in numbers over Burnham-on-Sea on 8 May). Passage north continues well into June, but little detail is published on the spring passage.

Return passage is noted by late July, but the main departure is rather sudden and usually about the third week of August, with few remaining into October. Very late birds were seen on 10 November 1981 and on the 13th in 1967.

Large feeding flocks of 1000–1500 are frequently seen over the reservoirs.

Alpine Swift *Apus melba*

Vagrant.

Five records of single birds: Axbridge, 1851 (before 23 September); Wembdon, 2 November 1952; Porlock, 5 October 1954; Minehead, 22 April 1964; Dunkery Beacon, 27 May 1980.

Kingfisher *Alcedo atthis*

Resident; local and scarce. Also passage-migrant and winter visitor.

The numbers of pairs probably changed very little between 1850 and 1966; disturbance and pollution of rivers have in part been compensated for by the increase in permanent water. It has probably held its own in recent years, with local fluctuations, but is very susceptible to cold winters, and was severely reduced in the winters of 1962/63 and 1979/80, and to a lesser extent in 1981/82.

Occurs mainly to the east of a line drawn roughly between the Parrett Estuary and Wellington, with pairs proved breeding at 27 localities, and breeding suspected at a further 18. The *Breeding Atlas* confirmed breeding in 16 of the county's 10-km squares with probable or possible breeding in a further seven. A more recent distibution map published in the 1986 Report gives a similar result.

Bee-eater   *Merops apiaster*

Vagrant.

Two records of single birds: one shot sometime before 1867 near Bridgwater; the other at Hambridge on 22 April 1986.

Roller   *Coracias garrulus*

Vagrant.

Three records: one shot at Orchard Portman many years before 1869; one at Staplegrove, August 1863; and one in a Milverton orchard, 11 June–3 July 1970, which may have been present for a fortnight before this.

Hoopoe   *Upupa epops*

Passage-migrant; scarce. Has bred.

A pair attempted to breed at Badgworth in 1931, but the eggs were deserted, no doubt to the delight of the local collectors. However, in 1977, following an influx into the country, a pair succeeded in rearing one young at Berrow (Slade, 1978). The same year a pair reared three young at Midsomer Norton; the nest was just over the border in Avon, but the birds regularly fed in Somerset (Eley, 1978).

About 96 were recorded between 1833 and 1966, and about another 64 up to 1987. The earliest was on 10 March, the latest on 31 October; the majority have been between March and May.

Wryneck *Jynx torquilla*

Passage-migrant; rare. Formerly bred.

Still quite common, at least in parts, until about 1915. Then declined rapidly until 1925, after which it became mainly a rare passage-migrant. Of the 25 recorded between 1924 and 1965, there were 16 in the spring and 9 in autumn. This is the reverse of recent records, where of about 52 recorded only 9 have been in spring.

Between 1851 and 1923, when it was still reasonably common, the average arrival date was 10 April, the earliest 10 March; the departure was during August and September.

Since 1966, spring passage 26 March–12 May; in autumn from July to October, mostly from late August to the end of September, with the latest at Burcott, near Wookey, on the exceptionally late date of 15 November 1986.

In 1973 a pair may have attempted to breed in an orchard at Shepton Mallet; unfortunately the trees were felled on 23 July, but the pair were agitated and remained in the area till the 30th. In 1983, at Fivehead, a pair frequently foraged on the village cricket square during the first week of July, but there was no evidence of breeding taking place.

Green Woodpecker *Picus viridis*

Resident; common.

A common and widespread resident, occurring from sea level to the high ground in the west (up to 380m in the Barle Valley in 1977). Severely reduced during the 1962/63 winter, but had apparently recovered by 1966. Appears to have survived some recent cold winters rather better, but has always been noted for its fluctuating numbers. The *Breeding Atlas* confirmed breeding in 30 of the county's 10-km squares with probable or possible breeding in a further seven.

Usually seen singly, in pairs or family parties, but 14 near Wedmore, on 28 July 1959, were feeding on ants.

Great Spotted Woodpecker *Dendrocopos major*

Resident; locally common. Passage-migrant and probable winter visitor.

Apparently a rare bird in the last century, becoming fairly common and widespread by the 1930s. Numbers probably remained fairly stable until the mid-1960s when there was a distinct increase. Has certainly benefited, at least in the short term, from the effects of the Dutch elm disease epidemic, with a plentiful supply of rotting timber in which to find food. The *Breeding Atlas* confirmed breeding in all of the 10-km squares except one, although breeding has since been proved there also.

As a passage-migrant occurs in very small numbers, usually between September and November; has been observed flying west on Brean Down and also over the Exmoor plateau. Probably occurs as a winter visitor, but this has yet to be proved.

Lesser Spotted Woodpecker *Dendrocopos minor*

Resident; local.

Rather thinly distributed, and although overlooked it is thought to be much less common than its larger relatives.

The *Breeding Atlas* confirmed breeding in 11 of the county's 10-km squares, with probable or possible breeding in a further nine. Widely reported during the breeding season, but rarely from more than 20 localities in any one year (only seven in 1983). The most favoured areas are the orchards and woodlands in the lower parts, although it can be difficult to locate in the taller trees. Also in woods on higher ground, particularly in the west, where in the past has bred near the tree-limit on Exmoor.

More widespread in winter when birds frequently join wandering tit flocks, and are then more easily seen.

Short-toed Lark *Calandrella brachydactyla*

Vagrant.

Two records of single birds: Brean Down, 16 June 1973, and Berrow, 9 May 1984.

Crested Lark *Galerida cristata*

Vagrant.

One record: one, Steart, 8 April 1972.

Woodlark *Lullula arborea*

Passage-migrant; scarce. Formerly bred.

Following a dramatic contraction of breeding range since the 1950s, it probably last bred during the early 1970s. Formerly bred most regularly on the Mendips from Crook Peak to Wells, on the Poldens from Ashcott to Somerton, on the Blackdowns, from Taunton to the north-east Quantocks and up to Wembdon, and from Dunster to Porlock. Isolated sites elsewhere from Holford to Bruton, Burnham-on-Sea and Berrow, Yeovil to Chard, Wellington, west Quantocks, and lower parts of Exmoor. Preferred habitat mainly open spaces with scattered trees, scrubby heathland, felled woodland or outskirts of woods, or semi-cleared areas of heather or gorse; most sites were on the lower slopes of hills.

Odd pairs at former sites till the early 1970s, then only singing birds at Canada Farm near Shapwick, 27 March 1977, Holford Combe, 5 April 1981, and Haddon Hill, 20 June 1986.

Since 1966, almost annual on passage, with most records in the autumn: twice in September from 15th, 24 October records, four in November, and two in December. Most records on the coast from Brean to West Huntspill; once at Cheddar Reservoir, and two birds on Westbury Moor. Birds often noted flying south, and with virtually no pairs left breeding north or west of the county, one may speculate that most of the passage birds are of Continental origin.

When more common, wintering flocks assembled on stubble fields, with over 70 at West Chinnock, 29 December 1924, and over 60 at Sampford Arundel, 26 January 1952. The most recent wintering record is five at Lynch, near Porlock, 23 January–6 February 1976. Rarely noted on passage in spring, with occasional records February–April on the coast, and once at Screech Owl, Huntworth, 4 February 1987.

Skylark   *Alauda arvensis*

Resident, winter visitor and passage-migrant; common and widespread.

Little actual information on breeding, but considered widespread throughout the county; the *Breeding Atlas* shows breeding proved in 44 squares (85 per cent), and probable in a further seven (14 per cent). Considered to have a breeding density above the national average on Exmoor.

In autumn, passage of northern and Continental birds en route to France and Iberia occurs from August to November, noted mainly on the coast and at the reservoirs. In winter, the resident population and winter visitors are found in the lowland and coastal areas, sometimes in flocks of up to several hundred; in icy conditions hard-weather movements occur, often involving

hundreds of birds, as at Berrow when about 800 flew south, 8 January 1982.

Spring passage much less marked, February–April, with breeding birds returning to territories by early March, although in colder springs, some of the moorland sites are not occupied till April.

Shore Lark *Eremophila alpestris*

Winter visitor and passage-migrant; rare.

In Britain a scarce winter visitor mainly to the east coast, where the population fluctuates and has noticeably declined in the last decade; in past years an infrequent winter visitor to Somerset, then recorded annually 1976–82, but there have been none since.

Since 1966, between 39 and 52 birds, as early as 17 October but most often arriving early/mid-November; some staying for long periods, sometimes into April, the latest being on 22nd. Usually single birds or small parties, but 13 at Porlock, 1 November 1976. Most records have been from Porlock, and the coast from Brean to Stolford, with one inland at Cheddar Reservoir, 17 October 1969–22 April 1970.

Sand Martin   *Riparia riparia*

Summer visitor; scarce and local. Passage-migrant; fairly common.

Usually arrives mid-March, the earliest being the 4th (1952), and one exceptional record at Durleigh, 27 January 1975. Excluding the January record, the average arrival date, 1966–86, was 19 March.

Used to breed in all districts of the county, although only in small numbers; besides the usual sandpits, there have been colonies in river banks and wall-drains, peat cuttings and stacks of dried peat blocks. Following the drastic population crash in the late 1960s and subsequent years, breeding records in Somerset have become fewer. In addition to the Sahel drought in the wintering areas, some loss of habitat and cool wet summers have added to the problem. Now virtually confined to small colonies on the River Tone at Bathpool, Taunton, Tonedale, Westford, and Burchess Hill. In addition, several pairs at Ashford Reservoir, with occasional summer records from old sites, but the actual breeding population may be less than ten pairs. In 1987, a small colony of three pairs was found near Dulverton.

A further decline in 1984, most apparent on passage, with no reservoir count over 25; some indication of a slight recovery in 1986 and 1987.

Breeding birds and migrants leave from mid-July to September. Scarcer in October than other hirundines; three November records; twice in December, latest at Porlock, 2 December 1948. When more numerous, roosting flocks of up to 500 occurred in reed-beds.

Swallow   *Hirundo rustica*

Summer visitor and passage-migrant; common.

Usually arrives in the last ten days of March, occasionally as late as 7 April. Has occurred as early as 25 February, but a pair building a nest at Minehead, 24 January 1975, was most exceptional.

Main influx through April into May. Passage most obvious along the coast and at the reservoirs, where counts of several thousand have been noted.

Confirmed breeding in every 10-km square of the county, preferring farm buildings, outhouses, sheds, and porches; the breeding density is obviously less on the higher moors and in urban areas. Perhaps less common than before, as indicated by surveys in the South Brewham area, east of Bruton.

In the 4sq. mile survey area, there were 52 nests in 1929, dropping to only 20 in 1969, with some recovery to 38 in 1981 (Hollom, 1985).

Autumn passage more leisurely, through August to early October. Stragglers into November; four December records, the latest on the 16th (1970).

Large numbers congregate at the reservoirs, and roosts are often formed in reed- and withy-beds, sometimes numbering several thousand (up to 8000 in a commercial withy-bed on West Sedge Moor, 3 September 1987).

Red-rumped Swallow   *Hirundo daurica*

Vagrant.

One, Porlock, 29 October 1987; there was an influx into Britain at this time. This is the first record for the 'new' county of Somerset.

House Martin   *Delichon urbica*

Summer visitor and passage-migrant; common.

Generally the last of the three hirundines to arrive in spring. Earliest date 9 March, but occasionally not till second week of April. Average arrival date 1966–86 was 2 April. Passage throughout April into May, when flocks of up to 1000 occur, mainly at the reservoirs. Many of the early birds pass straight through, with local breeding colonies not usually occupied till May.

The population is subject to national as well as local fluctuations, as indicated by the Common Bird Census. This is perhaps mirrored by Hollom's survey around South Brewham (*v. sup.*): in 1929 there were 104 nests, with a substantial reduction only four years later, then 108 in 1969, and only 54 in 1981.

Breeding birds leave from mid-August, with passage through September into October. As in spring, flocks numbering hundreds occur at the reservoirs, and passage is obvious on the coast. On Brean Down, cross-Channel passage sometimes fairly heavy and on 17 October 1981 in mist, rain and easterly winds, up to 2000 birds flew in from the sea in three hours and headed north, with similar numbers noted at Berrow. There were at least 5500 over Bossington and Porlock Marsh, 4 October 1987.

Last date often into November, with four December records, the last on the 28th (1944).

Richard's Pipit Anthus novaeseelandiae

Vagrant.

Eleven records of single birds: Huntspill/Parrett Estuary, 21 December 1958–11 February 1959; Brean Down, 16 October 1960; Steart, 19 October 1974; Cheddar Reservoir, 20 October 1975; Berrow, 17 October 1976; Dunster, 27 November 1977; Minehead, 11–28 March 1980; Brean Down, 25 November 1980; Wet Moor, 8 March 1981; Cheddar Reservoir, 12 December 1981; Huntspill, 18/19 October and 3 November 1985.

Tawny Pipit Anthus campestris

Vagrant.

Nine records of single birds, all but the first on the coast: Cheddar Reservoir, 4 May 1947; Steart, 1 August 1956, 4 October 1973 and 15 October 1974; Brean Down, 8 April 1983; Brue Estuary, 5 October 1983; Berrow, 23 September 1984; Burnham-on-Sea, 10 September 1986; Berrow, 25 September 1986.

Tree Pipit Anthus trivialis

Summer visitor and passage-migrant; fairly common but local.

Arrival and passage from mid-April to early May, occasionally March, the earliest being the 13th (1948). Passage most apparent on the coast: occasionally small flocks in double figures, with a maximum of 60, Brean Down, 2 May 1980.

Breeds in small numbers throughout the county, preferring edges of woods, young conifer plantations, heathland and the rougher peat-moors. Scattered pairs in east Somerset and the Mendips from Gare Hill to Cheddar; up to 40 pairs on the Blackdowns; fairly widespread on the Quantocks and Exmoor. On the levels, restricted to Shapwick, Ashcott, Glastonbury and Walton Heaths, with small numbers in the south on the higher ground between Yeovil and Chard.

In autumn, passage more leisurely, from late July to late September; occasional in October, the last on 17th (1986).

Meadow Pipit   *Anthus pratensis*

Resident, summer visitor, winter visitor and passage-migrant; locally abundant.

The most common and often the only passerine breeding on the higher exposed moors on the Quantocks and particularly on Exmoor, where breeding density is much higher than the national average. Fairly common on the Mendip plateau, and widely scattered on the levels, where at least 170 pairs found on the Central Levels during the 1983 survey. Little information from the south and east of the county.

Passage in spring from late February to mid-April, occasionally in large numbers. Much more apparent in autumn, from late July to early November, mostly late September to mid-October, when large movements noted on the coast and influxes at the reservoirs.

In winter some birds may stay in their breeding areas, but most descend to lower ground and the coast. Some leave the county altogether, and occasional hard-weather movements are noted.

Red-throated Pipit   *Anthus cervinus*

Vagrant.

Two records: two at Steart, 7 October 1979; one, Sutton Bingham Reservoir, 27 October 1979.

Rock Pipit   *Anthus petrosus*

Resident, passage-migrant, winter visitor; scarce and local.

Breeds on the coast at Brean Down (three to four pairs), from Stolford to Watchet (ten pairs or more), and Minehead to Glenthorne (10–12).

Post-breeding dispersal and passage birds from early October to early November, usually singly or in small parties, but up to 30 recorded together. Most winter records are from coastal breeding areas and estuaries.

Inland, 23 birds reported 1941–65, all at Cheddar Reservoir; since then, annual at Cheddar, occasional at Durleigh and Sutton Bingham Reservoirs, and once at Luxhay Reservoir. Very rare away from these, with only three records on the levels. Occurs from early October, mostly in the middle of that month; a few records in November; scarce December–February; a small peak in late March. One record that falls outside this pattern is of two at a weir on River Tone at Taunton, 16 July 1983.

Scandinavian Rock Pipit *A.p. littoralis*
Vagrant.

Four records since 1969, all at Cheddar Reservoir, 16 March–12 April; perhaps is really more frequent, but overlooked when in winter plumage, and this race may account for some of the autumn migrants and winter visitors.

One showing characteristics of this race, also at Cheddar, on the most unusual date of 14 July 1986.

Water Pipit   *Anthus spinoletta*

Passage-migrant and winter visitor; scarce.

Almost annual, with an average of nearly five per year since 1966, but scarce since 1985. Usually single birds but up to four together. Apart from two on 7 October, main arrival and passage in late October, with a scattering of records through the winter; in spring the peak is late March; scarce into late April, with one, 10 May 1976. One, King's Sedge Moor Drain, Weston-zoyland, 20 June 1963.

Mostly at Cheddar Reservoir, a few on the coast from Berrow to Stolford, with odd records on the levels, at Sutton Bingham Reservoir and Wells Sewage Farm.

Yellow Wagtails   *Motacilla flava ssp.*

Yellow Wagtail *M.f. flavissima*
Summer visitor and passage-migrant; locally common.

Breeds fairly commonly on the levels, but has recently suffered a decline in some places; has bred at Orchardleigh and Porlock, and still breeds on the

coast at Steart. Little actual information till the surveys in 1977 and 1983, when a general decrease noted, most drastically on the South Levels: on Wet Moor, numbers dropped from 28 pairs in 1977 to only one in 1985, and on West Sedge Moor from 14 pairs to only one or two in 1986. Some compensation in widespread increase north of the Poldens, particularly Tealham/Tadham and Aller Moors, where 31 pairs present in 1983. Mainly associated with damp cattle pasture; often on spoil-banks near rhynes, or in neighbouring hay meadows, or even arable crops.

Passage most obvious on the coast and at the reservoirs, scarce in the east but occasionally noted in autumn.

In spring from early April to early May (earliest 4 March 1973), with males usually arriving first. Maximum counts of 52 at Brean Down, 2 May 1980, and inland, 35 at Cheddar Reservoir, 1 May 1979.

Larger numbers in autumn, with passage late July–September; occasional in October and November, with latest at Shapwick, 15 December 1973. Counts often over 20, occasionally 50, with up to a 100 at Steart, 28 August 1975, and over 300 roosting in a withy-bed on West Sedge Moor, 4 September 1987.

Blue-headed Wagtail *M.f. flava*
Passage-migrant; rare. Has bred.

This is the most frequent and likely race from the Continent, with at least 60 in spring, 11 April–7 June, and at least 14 in autumn, 29 July–14 September.

Several old breeding records, and since 1966 has bred at least nine times, usually in mixed pairs with *flavissima*.

Birds showing characteristics of other races have occurred, but these and some aberrant birds are notoriously difficult to assign to subspecies. At least three Grey-headed Wagtails *M.f. beema*, 21 April–14 May, and one, 16 July. At Cheddar Reservoir, one Ashy-headed Wagtail *M.f. thunbergi*, 19 May 1981, and single males of the Spanish race *M.f. iberia*, 17 April 1978 and 26 April 1979. Two birds apparently of *M.f. lutea* from the Russian steppes, on Tealham Moor, 30 June 1983, and one at Cheddar Reservoir, 4 April 1985. Aberrant grey-backed individuals, Brean Down, 10 May 1980, and King's Moor, 13 June 1982.

Grey Wagtail   *Motacilla cinerea*

Resident, winter visitor and passage-migrant; widespread but local.

Breeds widely throughout the county, preferring the fast-flowing streams on Exmoor, the Mendips and Quantocks, the streams and rivers on the levels, and also sluggish watercourses with weirs; even found in urban areas when these are available.

Grey Wagtails disperse widely after breeding, and from September they move from the more exposed areas to more sheltered combes, lowland rivers, reservoirs and coastal areas. Usually in pairs or small parties, but up to 30 at Sutton Bingham Reservoir, 29 August 1962. Passage noted on the coast at Brean Down and Berrow, where birds often fly across from Wales, late August–late October, with a maximum of 12, 7 September 1980.

They suffer badly in severe winters, and this leads to fluctuations in breeding levels.

Very small passage March/April, again mainly apparent on the coast.

Pied Wagtails   *Motacilla alba ssp.*

Pied Wagtail *M.a. yarrellii*
Resident, winter visitor, summer visitor and passage-migrant; common.

Found commonly throughout the county except on the highest ground; scarce on Exmoor above 250m. Although frequently found along streams, rivers and reservoirs, it also occurs widely on waste ground, suburban lawns and playing fields, and on buildings in urban areas.

Post-breeding flocks and passage birds arrive from mid-July, most in late September and October, with flocks of up to 200 at the reservoirs and on the coast. Two juveniles ringed in autumn at Cheddar were found in southern Portugal two months later. In autumn and winter, roosting occurs, often at regular sites, including withy-beds, town parks and buildings, and factories. Maximum count of 947 at the Westland Works, Yeovil, 25 January 1977.

Residents and winter visitors are susceptible to hard weather, and numbers fall after cold winters.

Wintering birds leave from late February, and spring passage continues to late April, but in smaller numbers than in autumn.

White Wagtail *M.a. alba*
Passage-migrant, identified chiefly in spring; locally common.

In spring, most frequent on the coast, particularly from Brean to Stolford, and at Cheddar Reservoir; small numbers at other reservoirs, but rare elsewhere. They breed throughout Europe, but most of the birds in Somerset are probably en route to Iceland.

Occurs in small parties of up to ten, but up to 46 have been noted; usually from early April, with most from 10th to early May; earliest 2 March and latest 21 May, with two old records in early June.

Much less frequently identified in autumn when large number of moulting and juvenile Pied Wagtails make identification less easy. Most from mid-August to late September; a few in October; rare November, with latest on 9th.

Waxwing   *Bombycilla garrulus*

Winter visitor; rare and irregular.

Occasional winter visitor to the county, during its periodic invasions. Most frequently seen in towns and suburbs, feeding on berry-bearing shrubs such as Cotoneaster, some birds staying for several days before moving on as the food supply dwindles.

About 60 reported, 1832–1941, 34 from 1942 to 1964, then 22 in the winter of 1965/66, when unprecedented numbers reached Britain; only about 13 since. Usually noted from mid-November, (earliest on 6th) through to late March, although one was seen at Dulverton, 21 May 1931; May records are rare but not unprecedented.

Dipper   *Cinclus cinclus*

Resident; locally common.

The Dipper is a bird of unpolluted, fast-flowing streams with exposed rocks and weirs, and particularly associated with the moorland streams of Exmoor, from 500m down to sea level. In addition it occurs sparingly on the Mells River, the Nunney Brook and the River Frome around Frome, on the Brue at Bruton, on the Axe and Sheppey around Wells, on the Yeo at Cheddar, on the Yeo at Yeovil, on the Ding and Isle around Ilminster, on the Otter and Yarty on the Blackdowns, on the Tone and its tributaries around Taunton, and on the east Quantock streams.

It is sedentary and highly territorial even in winter, although there is some altitudinal movement from the more exposed moorland streams. By plotting each breeding site since 1966, one may guess at a population of 105–135 pairs, with up to 75 on Exmoor alone. Has become scarcer on lowland streams, where it is prone to pollution, and may have declined elsewhere, possibly as a result of disturbance, but many suitable areas are rarely visited.

Wren   *Troglodytes troglodytes*

Resident; very common.

It breeds throughout the county, preferring areas of woodland or scrubby vegetation, hedgerows and even the high moors where gorse or dense heather offer some protection. In winter, birds often desert the more exposed areas and are commonly found in reed-beds and other such areas of rank vegetation. There is some local dispersal and perhaps small-scale movement to and from the county, but on the whole it is fairly sedentary.

Such a tiny bird with little potential for storing fat is extremely prone to cold and icy conditions; however, it breeds prolifically and the population recovers well after such severe winters.

Dunnock *Prunella modularis*

Resident; very common. Also passage-migrant and winter visitor?

It is widespread and common throughout the county except for the more exposed moorland areas. Preferred habitat includes areas of woodland with dense undergrowth, hedgerows and coastal scrub, marshland, suburban areas and gardens.

Usually singly or in pairs, but occasionally in small parties, particularly in winter when in competition for food.

Local Dunnocks are largely sedentary, as indicated by an adult ringed at Brent Knoll in 1955, which was recaptured there almost seven years later. There is some post-breeding dispersal, and ringing has shown that of fledged young, females tend to disperse further from their natal areas, although only short distances are involved. In addition, in severe weather, females are forced to move away by the more dominant males, and are subject to a heavier mortality. At such times there may be some immigration of birds from other areas. In autumn they tend to become agitated and more conspicuous, and this may give the impression of some migration at this time.

Alpine Accentor *Prunella collaris*

Vagrant.

One very old record: a bird shot in the Deanery Garden at Wells, 1833.

Robin   *Erithacus rubecula*

Resident; abundant. Also passage-migrant and winter visitor.

Found commonly throughout the county, except on exposed hilltops and moors, preferring areas of open woodland, well-timbered hedgerows, parks and gardens. Breeding population probably resident, with a number of birds retrapped where ringed in subsequent years, but is augmented in autumn by migrants from the north (as far as Scotland), and from the east; passage most apparent September/October, less so in spring, in March/April.

Nightingale   *Luscinia megarhynchos*

Summer visitor; uncommon and local.

The breeding range in Britain is mostly to the south of a line from the River Severn to the Humber, and so Somerset is right on the westward limit. Undoubtedly the Nightingale has declined in Britain, most obviously at the edge of the range, and this may be attributed at least in part to climatic change, with persistently cool late springs making conditions less favourable.

It is a bird of deciduous woodland with dense undergrowth, coppiced woodland, woodland edges and areas of bushy vegetation. On the levels, found mainly on the peat-moors, and on wooded hillsides surrounding the Central and South Levels. In the early part of the century, said to be absent on the peat-moors, but Shapwick and Street Heaths now regularly hold up to seven pairs each. Although apparently suitable habitat exists on Exmoor and the Mendips, virtually all singing birds are below the 200m contour. Scarce in the west, although perhaps an increase in the 1970s; regular between Watchet and Blue Anchor but infrequent further west.

BTO surveys were undertaken in 1976 and 1980, with 169 singing birds located in 1980, an increase on the 81 in 1976, due partly to better coverage and to its generally being a better year for the species throughout the country (for the earlier Census, see Suter, 1976).

Passage from mid-April to May; average arrival 18 April (1971–86), earliest 24 March (1943). This date has become later, mainly due to the cold springs which sometimes hold birds back till late April. When singing stops in mid-June, the bird is difficult to detect and is rarely seen in autumn; departure from mid-July, with the latest 2 September.

Bluethroat   *Luscinia svecica*

Vagrant.

Thirteen records of single birds, twice in spring, the rest July–October: one labelled only as 'Somerset 1856', Albert Memorial Museum, Exeter; male *L.s. cyanecula*, Bishop's Lydeard, July 1877; adult between Edithmead and Burnham, 3 May 1958; single birds, Steart, 27 August–3 September 1961, 20 August 1962 and 25 September 1969; two different birds ringed at Combwich, 8 and 10 September 1969; Berrow, 12 September 1970; a young male *L.s. svecica* found dead, Black Down, 6 October 1971; a first-year bird ringed, Steart, 24 August 1976, and one ringed, 29 September 1979; a female on Wet Moor, 13 June 1982.

Black Redstart   *Phoenicurus ochruros*

Passage-migrant and winter visitor; scarce.

First recorded in 1853, with about 160 between 1925 and 1965. Now annually in small numbers, with as many as 40 in some years. Most occur on the coast from Brean to Hinkley Point, with smaller numbers from Minehead to Porlock, and a few records scattered throughout the county, although rarely in the east.

Normally arrives from mid-October, with a peak in late October/early November. The origin of birds on Brean Down, 5 August–22 October 1967, and at Sutton Bingham Reservoir, 26 August 1967, may have been fairly local. Some birds stay to winter, often for several months.

Less frequent in spring, with light passage from early March to mid-April; two old May records, but more recently: one at Cheddar Reservoir, 13 May 1973; one at Hinkley Power Station, 26 May 1974; a male at Oare, 6 July 1978; and a pair, which may have bred, at the Taunton Hydrographic Department in 1982.

Redstart   *Phoenicurus phoenicurus*

Summer visitor and passage-migrant; uncommon and local.

Formerly more widespread, but now restricted to wooded combes on Exmoor (40–60 pairs) and Quantocks (about 35), up to 10 pairs on the

Blackdowns, and up to 35 pairs scattered on the Mendips in small copses and areas with odd hawthorn bushes. Odd pairs may be found on the wooded ridge running along the border in the east of the county. However, numbers, particularly on Exmoor, may well be under-estimated, as much woodland is rarely if ever visited. Used to breed widely in pollarded willows on the levels, but has declined markedly over the last 20 years, and now the occasional records probably relate to passage birds. In the late 1960s the population crashed by almost half, and although some increase has been noted, it remains a local breeder in Somerset.

The average arrival date, 1971–86, was 11 April, the same as that given in Palmer & Ballance; the earliest was 25 March. Passage through April to mid-May; most often noted on the coast and occasionally inland. Following post-breeding dispersal, passage from late July to mid-October; twice in November (latest, 19th). There is an exceptional record of a female photographed in the snow at Priorswood Estate, Taunton, 20 January 1985.

Whinchat   *Saxicola rubetra*

Summer visitor and passage-migrant; locally common.

The Whinchat is a bird of rough pasture or moorland that has posts, fences or bushes providing suitable perches. A survey on Exmoor in 1978 suggested 450–600 pairs, representing about 1.5 per cent of the British population. Up to 30 pairs on the Quantocks, odd pairs on Blackdowns, and around Yeovil, but few if any on Mendips and in the east of the county. Has suffered a decline on the levels, probably as a result of upgrading of grassland, and increasing practice of cutting silage early in the season. The Levels Survey in 1977 found 153 pairs, dropping to 110 pairs in 1983; there was a 60 per cent decrease on the South Levels, but a small compensatory increase on the Central Levels.

Main arrival from mid-April (earliest 27 March), with passage till mid-May. In autumn, passage most obvious on coast till mid-September, occasionally into October; five times in November, with latest at ROF Puriton, 11 November 1982. Has probably wintered on Aller Moor, where recorded 24 February and 7 March 1983.

Stonechat *Saxicola torquata*

Resident, summer and winter visitor and passage-migrant; scarce and local.

Favoured habitat includes uncultivated open land with small bushes, shrubs and scattered perennials, mainly on higher ground. It has decreased, in part because of reclamation of moorland and other rougher areas. Most are now found in the west: up to 150 pairs on Exmoor in 1978 survey, but normally fewer than 40 pairs reported; at least 27 pairs on Quantocks, and up to seven on Blackdowns; up to four pairs, Brean Down; up to 12 pairs on Mendips from Wells to Wavering Down. Formerly bred on coastal dunes from Axe Estuary to Burnham-on-Sea, and on the peat-moors, at Fivehead and on West Sedge Moor, at Hamdon Hill, Ilminster, and Ilton, and around Taunton.

Some breeders are resident, but most leave the higher ground in August or September; small autumn passage on coast, with occasional irruptions from late September to November. Those that winter, either singly or in pairs, occur widely on the coast and inland, October–March; however, being a ground-feeder with a mainly insectivorous diet, the Stonechat is highly susceptible to cold weather and snow, and decreases dramatically after cold winters, as happened in 1962/63, early 1978 and early 1986.

There is a small spring passage, chiefly on the coast in March, as indicated by 20, Brean Down, 18 March 1979.

Wheatear *Oenanthe oenanthe*

Summer visitor; very local. Passage-migrant; common.

It has decreased since 1920 and is now virtually confined as a breeder to Exmoor, where it prefers moorland and coastal slopes broken by walls, rocks, ruined buildings and scree slopes; a survey in 1978 found around 100 pairs on the Moor. It used to breed with some regularity on rougher hilltops on the Mendips, on the coast at Steart Island and Stolford, and occasionally on the levels and elsewhere. Since 1966, there have been possible breeding records of up to three pairs on the Quantocks, in 1977 and 1978; three pairs, Rookham, and a male in song on Black Down, 1980; and a pair with two juveniles on Brean Down, 23 July 1980, may have bred locally.

Common on passage in both seasons, mainly on coast, but also inland, with counts often into double figures at peak times; up to 50 together at Bristol Plain Farm near Priddy in April 1981. The earliest was 13 February (1932), and the average arrival date 1966–86 was 11 March. On autumn passage from mid-July to late September, with stragglers to October; latest, 27 November (1965).

Greenland Wheatear *O.o. leucorrhoa*
Passage-migrant; scarce.

Larger, brighter Wheatears presumed to be of this race have been reported mainly in the spring: in the period 1966–87, from 27 April to 19 June, mostly in the first two weeks of May. All records but one were on the coast; mainly single birds, but up to five.

Rare in autumn, with four records 10 September–28 October. Probably occurs more frequently but is overlooked when not in breeding plumage.

White's Thrush *Zoothera dauma*

Vagrant.

One record: one, Hestercombe, 7 January 1870.

Ring Ouzel   *Turdus torquatus*

Summer visitor; very local and scarce. Passage-migrant; scarce.

Several recent surveys suggest a fairly stable breeding population of about 30 pairs on Exmoor, mostly on the high moorland above 350m, and stretching from Dunkery to Hoar Oak in the west (Davis & Jarman, 1978; Allen, 1984). Generally found in the narrow, steep upper combes, with thick heather, hawthorn and rowan bushes and some open areas for feeding. Probably never a regular breeder on the Quantocks, where it last bred in 1955, and is now seen only on passage. Bred near Priddy in 1910.

Arrival from mid-March (earliest 9 March 1983), with migrants passing through mainly in late March and April; stragglers into May. Passage most obvious on Brean Down and the Mendips, the Quantocks, on Exmoor and the coast from Minehead to Porlock. Occasionally in parties in double figures; exceptionally 34, mostly males, Wavering Down, 3 April 1971; has been less common on passage in recent years. Spring passage includes Scandinavian migrants that take a more westerly route at this time.

Breeding birds drift away from Exmoor in August. Autumn passage involving smaller numbers than in spring, occurs in September and October, with a few stragglers into November, and one December record on 15th or 16th.

Blackbird   *Turdus merula*

Resident, summer and winter visitor and passage-migrant; abundant.

A common breeding bird throughout the county, confirmed in all the 10-km squares during the *Breeding Atlas* survey. Originally a bird of woodland edges, it has spread to farmland, hedgerows, parks and suburban gardens, and even into town centres.

Ringing has shown that most of the local breeding population is fairly sedentary, although there may be some dispersal to the north-west, Ireland, and the nearby Continent. Passage is evident from August to November, especially October/November, when birds from Scandinavia move to Britain to winter; there have been several winter-trapped birds that were either ringed or controlled in Sweden, Denmark, or the Low Countries (for the movements of this and other thrushes, see Parsons, 1986).

Return passage probably from late February, but there is little evidence of any movement.

Fieldfare   *Turdus pilaris*

Winter visitor and passage-migrant; locally common.

A characteristic bird of the Somerset Levels in winter, the timing of its main influx is highly dependent on Continental weather and the abundance of food sources in its Scandinavian breeding range. Arrival usually mid-October– mid-December, but has occurred as early as 22 August; the late August/early September records may be from the small British breeding population. Some birds pass on through, as indicated by two mid-December birds ringed at Berrow that were recovered in France in subsequent winters. Sometimes rather scarce in December/January, but further influxes preceding cold weather can occur throughout the winter.

Fieldfares may form large roving flocks of hundreds or occasionally of several thousand birds, often mixed with Redwings, scouring the countryside looking for berry-bearing shrubs and bushes, and even invading gardens in cold weather. They seem less able to withstand severe winters than Blackbirds, and a prolonged cold spell can cause heavy mortality. Communal roosts are often noted, with up to 16,000, mainly of this species, at Berrow, 27 February 1969.

Flocks gradually disperse from early March, with passage through to late April or early May; latest on 18th (1941).

Song Thrush *Turdus philomelos*

Resident, winter visitor and passage-migrant; common.

Widespread throughout the county, preferring any habitat associated with bushes or trees; rare on open ground but has been recorded nesting in heather above Sweetworthy (500m). Many local breeders probably sedentary, but there are two ringing recoveries of locally-bred juveniles in France and northern Spain the following winter.

Passage evident from late August, with most in October/early November, from northern and eastern Britain, the Low Countries, and probably Scandinavia. Some migrants winter locally, and further cold-weather influxes occur; return passage more leisurely in March/April.

Redwing *Turdus iliacus*

Winter visitor and passage-migrant; locally common.

A common migrant from early October to mid-November. Often recognised at night from the distinctive flight call as they pass overhead. Numbers in December/January rather more dependent on Continental weather conditions, and in mild winters they may be scarce at this time. Hard-weather movements are often very marked, as at Berrow on the morning of 12 December 1981, when at least 25,000 flew south.

Redwings tend to prefer the lowland areas, and feed in sizeable flocks, often numbering several hundreds or even thousands, usually associated with Fieldfares and Starlings. Roosts of several thousand are frequent, but may be as large as the 30,000 at Berrow, 2 March 1969, and 21,000 at Rowberrow Warren, 7 January 1961.

In spring, flocks often become agitated and stirred into conversational subsong. Departure much less obvious than arrival, birds leaving mainly in March, and a few in April; last noted, 8 May.

Ringing evidence suggests birds are mainly from Finland and the USSR, many on their way to winter in France and Iberia; there is a remarkable recovery of an immature ringed at Alford, 24 December 1980, found dead 4216km to the east, at Miass, Chelyabinsk, USSR, 18 May 1981. The erratic migratory behaviour of Redwings is evident by some individuals being found in different places in subsequent winters; one ringed at Mansmead Wood on 16 February 1980 was shot in Italy the following December, yet others have been controlled where they were originally ringed.

The earliest bird in autumn was a first-year bird controlled at Millwater, Crewkerne, 14 September 1983, which had been ringed at Blairgowrie, Tayside, on 19 August, and was perhaps of British origin.

Mistle Thrush *Turdus viscivorus*

Resident; common. Also passage-migrant and probably winter visitor.

It is a bird of well-timbered parklands, broad-leaved and coniferous woodland, plantations, orchards and gardens; as such, it is a scarce breeder on the poorly timbered levels, and absent on the open hilltops and moorlands. In the *Breeding Atlas*, breeding was proved in all but one square.

After breeding, roving flocks are formed, exceptionally as large as 250; they move to open ground to feed, particularly on Exmoor, the Mendips and the levels. These flocks disband in late summer, with young birds moving south while adults remain to stake their claim on local territories and food supplies.

Some passage, late August–late October, probably of the more migratory Scottish population, some of whom may stay to winter.

Cetti's Warbler *Cettia cetti*

Resident; rare and very local.

The first Somerset Cetti's Warbler was found in a mist net at Combwich, 8 April 1968, following a dramatic extension of breeding range during this century in north-west Europe. The next was trapped at Dunster, 27 November 1976; since then, Cetti's Warblers have been reported each subsequent year except 1980. They colonised the various brick-pits around Bridgwater, where first proved to breed in 1982. The first record away from the coastal clay belt was at East Lyng, 9 May 1979, and there have been up to three singing birds on the peat-moors since 1984. There were probably 15 males by 1983, with breeding at Cheddar Clay Pits the same year. A male at Minehead summered in 1984, and a pair probably bred at Dunster in 1985.

Has suffered dramatic reductions in south-east England and in France following severe cold spells in early 1985 and 1986. However, in Somerset there have only been slight reductions at their stronghold around Bridgwater; odd birds present at Apex (Burnham-on-Sea), and Berrow. Many apparently suitable sites exist on the levels, which may be colonised should a series of mild winters allow the population to become more viable.

A female controlled near Bridgwater, 10 June 1984, had been ringed at Lodmoor, Dorset, 12 August 1981. Up to 1987, A.W. Evans had ringed a total of 43 Cetti's Warblers in Somerset.

Grasshopper Warbler *Locustella naevia*

Summer visitor and passage-migrant; local and uncommon.

Grasshopper Warblers are more often heard than seen, 'reeling' from areas of dense scrub, damp marshy areas, rough pasture and young forestry plantation. Sites are scattered throughout the county from the conifer plantations on Gare Hill and the rough heathland on Shapwick, to the moorland on Exmoor in the west, where probably under-recorded. Subject to much fluctuation, with anything from 18 to 51 'reeling' birds in the last ten years, and breeding often difficult to prove; has become scarcer in recent years. In 1935, S. Lewis found nine nests in one morning on the peat-moors.

Average arrival, 1966–86, was 14 April, compared with 20 April, 1924–62; the earliest was 5 April. Passage occasionally quite marked on Brean Down late April/early May, with ten there, 27 April 1973. Rarely observed in autumn, with main departure probably late July or August; twice reported in September, and one trapped at Steart, 10 October 1984.

Savi's Warbler   *Locustella luscinioides*

Vagrant.

Seven records of this 'reed-bed reeler', all between 6 May and 3 July: one, 29 May–5 June 1970; one trapped, 13 May 1971; another, 14 May 1974; a singing male, 10 May–24 June 1977, joined by another male, 17–26 May; one, 6 May 1980; another singing bird, 11 June–3 July 1983.

The bird on 6 May 1980 was heard singing in competition with a Grasshopper Warbler and, although rejected by the *British Birds* Rarities Committee, we feel the record is valid.

Aquatic Warbler   *Acrocephalus paludicola*

Passage-migrant; scarce and very local.

First reported at Steart, 3 September 1961; two more occurred before 1971, since when the species has been reported annually. Virtually all the records are from *Phragmites* and *Spartina* in Bridgwater Bay and Berrow; more often trapped than observed. One observer, A.W. Evans, ringed 48 birds between 1969 and 1987, 14 of them in 1976.

A very early bird at Berrow, 7 July 1974, but most from 8 August to 5 September, with six stragglers till the last on 25 September.

Inland, at Sutton Bingham Reservoir, a juvenile, 5 September 1983, and two, 18 September 1984, one remaining till 25th.

Sedge Warbler *Acrocephalus schoenobaenus*

Summer visitor and passage-migrant; locally common.

Less dependent than Reed Warblers on pure stands of *Phragmites*, preferring the drier margins, and nesting in luxuriant vegetation of many waterside habitats. Generally distributed on the levels, and in coastal marshes at Berrow and Porlock; scattered pairs elsewhere, around Taunton and in the south, and at Sutton Bingham Reservoir. No recent breeding records from Mendips, Quantocks, and Exmoor, but still occurs in small numbers on passage.

It has undoubtedly declined following the population crash in the late 1960s, and numbers have fluctuated since then, although remaining fairly low. The Levels Surveys in 1977 and 1983 found 415 and 210 pairs respectively. Counts on West Sedge Moor have dropped from 91 in 1977 to as low as 21 in 1980, and 26 in 1986, with some recovery to at least 50 in 1987.

Average arrival around 18 April, but two have occurred as early as 28 March in recent times. Passage into May, with some migrants found away from breeding habitat, as were seven in bushes on Brean Down, 7 May 1981.

Breeders leave from late July; passage through till September, occasionally into October, with latest on 13th (1979).

Marsh Warbler   *Acrocephalus palustris*

Formerly scarce and local summer visitor, now vagrant.

Used to be more frequent, with a number of breeding records till the early twentieth century, especially around Taunton and Norton Fitzwarren, and scattered records from Castle Cary, Glastonbury and Cheddar. Bred at Minehead Clay Pits, 1929 and 1947–61, and fairly regularly on South Levels till the 1960s; then one record in June 1966, followed by a pair breeding in 1969.

The only recent record is of a male singing at Millwater, Crewkerne, 29 June–14 July 1984.

Reed Warbler   *Acrocephalus scirpaceus*

Summer visitor and passage-migrant; locally common.

Most commonly found in areas of *Phragmites*, particularly in the scattered brick-pits around Bridgwater, railway ballast-pits, and pools and rhynes on the levels; occasionally in other rank waterside vegetation. Very rare in the east (apparently not recorded since 1923); however, there were 'many' by the Mells River in August 1986, one in a hedgerow near Holcombe, 27 August 1987, and six birds singing in a reed-bed at Redlynch in 1988. Absent from the Mendips except for odd records at Priddy Pool; rare in the south-west and west, but regular at Porlock Marsh.

The average arrival date in 21 seasons, 1939–62, was 28 April, but now apparently arriving somewhat earlier, with the arrival date 1975–86 of 15 April, even excluding one very early bird, 28 March 1981.

Breeding birds leave and migrants pass in August and September, occasionally into October, with the last positively identified on the 24th; one almost certainly this species heard calling, Apex, Burnham-on-Sea, 4 November 1984.

Great Reed Warbler   *Acrocephalus arundinaceus*

Vagrant.

One record: a bird trapped, Combwich, 25 August 1969.

Icterine Warbler   *Hippolais icterina*

Vagrant.

One record: a very late bird, West Huntspill, 4 November 1984.

Melodious Warbler   *Hippolais polyglotta*

Vagrant.

Three records: single birds, Berrow, 27 August 1981, and Brean Down, 15 August 1983 and 30 August 1985.

In addition there have been five records of unidentified *Hippolais* warblers: single birds at Steart and Durleigh Reservoir, 22 August 1971, were probably Melodious; one on Brean Down, 23 September 1986, was thought to be Icterine; those at Durleigh on 30 August 1971, and at Berrow, 28 September 1985, were not specifically identified.

Dartford Warbler   *Sylvia undata*

Vagrant.

Following an adult female trapped at Steart, 11 August–17 November 1974, and single birds at Bossington Hill, 20–26 November 1974, and 22 October 1976, there were a series of interesting sightings on the Quantocks: a male, 18 April and 8 May 1976, again in 1977 on 24 and 31 May, and 6 and 27 November, and another on 17 February 1980.

In addition, single birds, Brean Down, 12/13 October 1977, Berrow, 6 February 1978, Brean Down in late March 1978, and Minehead, 6 December 1982.

A rare resident in Britain, but there is a tendency for juveniles to disperse after completion of moult in September. These records during the 1970s coincided with a time when the species was doing well in its rather restricted breeding range on the south coast, although several cold winters have substantially reduced numbers in recent years.

Barred Warbler   *Sylvia nisoria*

Vagrant.

Three records, all on typical dates: immature, Porlock Marsh, 8 August 1969; one, Berrow, 22 August 1976; one, Brean Down, 26 August 1986.

Lesser Whitethroat   *Sylvia curruca*

Summer visitor; local. Also passage-migrant.

Breeds locally in lowland Somerset, nesting in hedgerows, scrubby copses, brambles, and, on the coast, in blackthorn scrub. Seldom found above 150m, and uncommon in the south. Rather scarce in the west, but has perhaps increased there in recent years. Numbers in general fluctuate year to year, with as few as 33 singing males reported in 1979.

Arrival usually around 22 April (earliest 3 April 1985), with passage till mid-May. Departure mainly August/early September; stragglers to early October, with latest on 15th.

Whitethroat   *Sylvia communis*

Summer visitor and passage-migrant; now rather uncommon.

The Whitethroat is a bird of scrubby, well-vegetated areas, hedgerows, woodland edges and clearings, and young conifer plantations.

Formerly very common, but suffered a dramatic crash in 1969, when the national population fell by around 77 per cent. Increases noted in most subsequent years; several counts in 1987 suggest a 50 per cent increase on 1986 figures. Still scarce on higher ground, but perhaps such peripheral areas may be recolonised when the population returns to pre-crash levels. The highest breeding numbers/densities are on the low ground, especially the peat-moors.

Normally arrives in mid-April, with passage to mid-May; earliest 29 March (1936). Breeders leave from late July, with passage through to early October; stragglers through October, with latest on 18 November (1977).

Garden Warbler $\quad$ *Sylvia borin*

Summer visitor and passage-migrant; local.

Breeds throughout the county in similar habitat to Blackcap, in fairly open woodland with a dense scrub-layer, overgrown copses and large gardens. Numbers fluctuate each year; perhaps this is more apparent in marginal habitat.

Arrival mainly in the third week of April (earliest 2nd), but has arrived as late as 9 May. Passage till mid-May, most obvious at coastal areas, with nine on Brean Down, 7 May 1981. Breeders leave from mid-July; passage through till September; rare in October. Three times in November, the latest at Combwich, on 17th (1974).

Blackcap $\quad$ *Sylvia atricapilla*

Summer visitor and passage-migrant; locally common. A few resident or perhaps winter visitors.

Most frequently breeds in mature broad-leaved or mixed woodland, with a thick shrub layer, and in tall hedgerows, overgrown gardens and areas of thick scrubby cover. May have increased in recent years, and is normally more common than Garden Warbler.

Arrival from late March, with passage till third week of May, although not usually common until late April. Return passage from late July to late September, occasionally into October, but there has been an increasing tendency for birds to overwinter. The first to do so was a male shot near Taunton, 11 February 1885. There were a further eight wintering till 1921, and about 90 were reported, 1929–65. Now much more frequent, with as many as 49 in January/February 1985.

Yellow-browed Warbler $\quad$ *Phylloscopus inornatus*

Vagrant.

One feeding with Blue Tits and Goldcrests, Brean Down, 17 October 1981. Since many have occurred in Devon and Dorset, it is undoubtedly overlooked.

Wood Warbler *Phylloscopus sibilatrix*

Summer visitor and passage-migrant; locally common.

Common visitor to the sessile oakwoods of Exmoor, the Brendons and north-east Quantocks, preferring tall trees with a closed canopy, and virtually no shrub layer. Scattered pairs at Emborough and Bruton Forest, in the sheltered woods of the northern Mendips, at Copley Wood and around Wells, and on the northern escarpment of the Blackdowns.

Arrival from mid-April, and small coastal passage, till early May, with the earliest 28 March (1936). Departure and some movement, July–September, the latest record being on 29 September 1981.

Chiffchaff *Phylloscopus collybita*

Summer visitor and passage-migrant; common. Very scarce in winter.

The Chiffchaff is never as widespread or abundant as the Willow Warbler, but breeds commonly in most woods with a good shrub layer, tending to avoid the sessile oakwoods and beech woods of the west. Overgrown gardens, coniferous plantations and woodland edges are also frequently chosen, but it is very local on the comparatively treeless levels and higher ground.

Arrival and passage mid-March–early May, but the exact date of arrival is shrouded by the presence of overwintering birds. Passage in autumn is from late July to September, or early October. Some birds of the nominate race overwinter, and are most frequently found in damp vegetation in lowland woods and reed-beds, particularly on the coast, at reservoirs or sewage farms, with perhaps as many as 35 in any one winter.

In recent years there have been an increasing number of Chiffchaffs of the greyer eastern races *P.c. abietinus* from Scandinavia and *P.c. tristis* from Siberia. Several late-August records, but most have been from mid-October, with some remaining through the winter till late March. The plumages of these races are variable and in most cases it is hard to say to which birds belong. Most are probably *abietinus*, but there have been a fair number that at least show characteristics of *tristis*. An old record of one shot at Lympsham, 6 April 1925, and single birds at Durleigh Reservoir, 28 January, 2 February 1950, and 17 August 1952, were all claimed as *abietinus*.

Willow Warbler *Phylloscopus trochilus*

Summer visitor and passage-migrant; common, locally abundant.

Very common and widespread, breeding throughout in any area of woodland, and in bushes, scrubby wasteland and gardens. Often abundant on passage, especially on the coast, and falls of several hundred on places such as Brean Down are fairly commonplace. Normally arrives around 28 March, the earliest on the 11th (1951); passage fairly swift as indicated by one ringed at Watchet, 20 April 1984, controlled the next day some 320km to the north at North Walney, Barrow-in-Furness, Cumbria.

Departure noticeably earlier than Chiffchaff, from July to mid-September; rare in October, with last on 22nd (1935).

There are three winter records, all single birds: Berrow, 5 January 1982; Wet Moor, 24–28 December 1982; Dunster Beach, 11 January 1988.

There is only one confirmed record of the Northern race *P.t. acredula*, a male shot at Lympsham, 8 April 1926, but perhaps it is overlooked.

Goldcrest *Regulus regulus*

Resident, passage-migrant and probably winter visitor; locally common.

Normally widespread, and as a breeding species can be expected wherever there are conifers; the numbers show marked fluctuations and birds may be almost exterminated in severe winters, as happened in 1916/17, 1939/40, 1962/63, early 1979 and 1986; recovery to pre-crash levels normally takes several seasons.

Rarely noted on passage in spring, but since the early 1950s has been observed on the coast in September/October, with at least 50 on Brean Down in early October 1981. Some birds probably stay to winter.

Firecrest *Regulus ignicapillus*

Passage-migrant; very scarce and local. Has bred.

First report of two, Martock, 28 March 1924, with a further 21, mainly in the west, up to 1966. Now almost annual, with perhaps as many as 16 in 1982.

Passage and influx from late September, wintering through till late March; occasional April records, with a late bird singing on Brean Down, 6 May 1988. Winter distribution largely coastal, in sheltered scrub or woodland edge; uncommon inland, where it prefers river valleys and sewage farms.

There has been a marked expansion of range on the Continent, and birds first bred in England in 1962. Four interesting records of single birds away from usual wintering sites may be of prospective breeding birds: Langport, 13 August 1972; Horner Water, 31 May 1973; North Curry, 7 June 1975; Tadham Moor, 2 June 1983. One pair bred in Somerset in 1985 (Spencer, 1988), and two birds were singing at one site in 1988.

Spotted Flycatcher *Muscicapa striata*

Summer visitor and passage-migrant; common.

Widespread summer visitor, breeding in open woodland, farmland, copses, and on the levels in willows. Often nests in town gardens, parks and orchards, and has been recorded using hanging baskets and window boxes. Numbers vary from year to year, with a complete absence in Exmoor valleys in some years.

First migrants usually arrive in the first week of May, with breeders a week later, passage continuing until the end of the month. There have been nine April records, and one on 29 March (1981).

Return passage mid-July to late September, with gatherings of up to 15 (or occasionally as many as 40) at some sites in August. Twice in October and once on 29 November (1981).

Pied Flycatcher *Ficedula hypoleuca*

Summer visitor and passage-migrant; local.

Probably bred on Exmoor in the nineteenth century, and has bred there regularly at least since the mid-1920s. Most sites are in oak-wooded combes in the north-east, but also in the Exe and Barle Valleys, and coastal woods. Before 1970, fewer than 30 pairs, but the introduction of nestboxes in the late 1970s has greatly increased numbers, and perhaps more than 100 now breed. Up to five pairs on Quantocks, 1948–58, then absent till 1969; since then has bred most years in variable numbers, with up to 30 pairs regularly using nestboxes. There were isolated breeding records at Street in 1867, and near Wells in 1931, 1940 and 1942. Since 1980, singing males have been annual on the Blackdowns, with breeding proved in 1986 and possibly 1987. One pair bred near Charterhouse in 1988.

Breeding birds arrive from mid-April, with passage till mid-May, migrants occurring in all parts of the county. Nesting birds probably leave in July, with passage from then until the end of October. Most frequently noted on or near the coast.

Bearded Tit *Panurus biarmicus*

Resident; rare. Passage-migrant and winter visitor; scarce.

Only four records before 1928, then five at Brean Down in October 1965, an invasion year. Recorded almost annually at Berrow from 1966 to 1978, all from October to March. Up to three pairs have bred there since 1979.

There have been about 34 recorded at nine other sites, 1967–80, with up to four together; 7 October–9 February, except for one in April 1974. Apart from a pair at Sutton Bingham Reservoir and one at Porlock Marsh, all have been on the coast from Brean to Steart, or at pits around Bridgwater.

Long-tailed Tit   *Aegithalos caudatus*

Resident; locally common. Also passage-migrant?

Typically builds a domed structure of moss and lichen in scrub and hedgerows, and is less dependent on mature woodland for breeding than its relatives; widely distributed throughout the county, except on open moorland.

In winter, flocks of up to 65 occur in mixed flocks of tits and Goldcrests, feeding along hedgerows and in woods. Unlike the other tits, which tend to be omnivorous, they tend to remain insectivorous throughout the year, and as such are severely affected by hard winters, with recovery taking up to five years. Possibly an occasional autumn migrant on the coast.

Two records of white-headed birds, showing characteristics of the race *A.c. caudatus*: near Bridgwater, October 1871; and Horner Wood, 20 April 1986.

Marsh Tit   *Parus palustris*

Resident; locally common.

Breeds locally in deciduous woodland and copses across the county, and also in large gardens. Most numerous on the wooded hills, particularly on the Mendips and in the east, and in wooded combes in the south-west and west. Absent on exposed high ground, and rare on open farmland and peat-moors. In winter more widespread, usually associating with mixed tit flocks, foraging along hedgerows and in woodland.

Willow Tit   *Parus montanus*

Resident; scarce and local.

First recorded in 1918, its stronghold for many years was the peat-moors around Shapwick, where it bred in dead and rotten stumps in the marshy ground. Increased observation in the late 1960s found it on most of the levels between the Poldens and the Mendips. It also occurs on marshy ground on the Blackdowns, in Exmoor and Quantock valleys and combes, on the

Mendips, and in scattered localities in the east of the county. Reported as a regular breeder only at Wimbleball Lake, and at various sites on the Blackdowns. Since the late 1970s, numbers have steadily fallen on the peat-moors, and it is now scarce there, although pockets of its habitat have remained largely unchanged.

Coal Tit *Parus ater*

Resident; locally common. Passage-migrant and winter visitor.

Common in woodland, particularly conifers, and large gardens, but also in sessile oak woods west of the Parrett. Scarce on the levels and on agricultural land, but may be encountered almost anywhere in winter, when foraging in mixed flocks.

Large numbers invaded Somerset in 1957, but usually only light and variable passage from September to November, on the coast from Brean Down to Berrow. Migrant birds have been noted feeding amongst tidal debris on the rocks at the tip of Brean Down.

Blue Tit *Parus caeruleus*

Resident; abundant. Passage-migrant and winter visitor.

Widely distributed in deciduous woods, copses, gardens and hedgerows. In autumn and winter, foraging parties are common in reed-mace and *Phragmites*, in moorland combes, and in more open woodland and scrub.

In autumn, coastal migration in small numbers, generally from mid-September to mid-October; occasionally flocks up to 50, exceptionally 150–200. Ringing has shown that as many as 100 different Blue Tits may pass through a small suburban garden in the course of a single winter.

Great Tit *Parus major*

Resident; very common. Passage-migrant and possible winter visitor.

Proved breeding in every 10-km square in Somerset, in deciduous woodland, hedgerows and gardens. In winter feeds mainly on seeds and fruit and can be encountered anywhere, often in mixed flocks. Particularly fond of beechmast and in years when this is abundant, flocks of up to 100 may congregate to feed amongst the leaf litter.

Essentially sedentary, with all locally-ringed birds being recovered within 20km of their ringing site. However, there is some passage on the coast from Brean to Berrow; generally small numbers, but up to 100 have been recorded.

Nuthatch   *Sitta europaea*

Resident; locally common.

Widespread and encountered wherever stands of mature timber provide suitable nest sites; will occasionally use nestboxes and holes in walls. Absent only from open high ground, younger coniferous woodland, and the relatively treeless levels and the coast. Sedentary, but in winter may be found in foraging mixed tit flocks.

Wallcreeper   *Tichodroma muraria*

Vagrant.

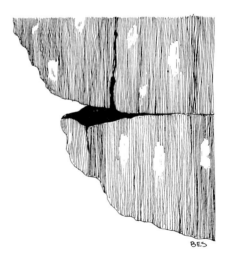

Three records, the last two presumably the same bird: one, Mells, September 1901; one Chelm's Combe Quarry, Cheddar, early November 1976 to 6 April 1977, and November 1977 until 9 April 1978 (see Rabbitts & Vinicombe, 1978).

Treecreeper   *Certhia familiaris*

Resident; fairly common. Also passage-migrant?

Breeds throughout the county, typically in mature hedgerows, copses and deciduous or mixed woodland, less commonly in coniferous woods. Usually a solitary feeder, but in winter often associates with parties of tits or other species. A sedentary species, but has occasionally been seen on Brean Down in October and March, so there may be some small movement or dispersal in some years.

Golden Oriole   *Oriolus oriolus*

Summer visitor and passage-migrant; very rare.

About 13 at various sites 1860–1910; the only dated birds were in May or June. Since 1923 a further 15 have occurred, mostly males; three on the coast, the rest widely distributed inland. All 20 April–29 June, except one on 19 August.

Red-backed Shrike   *Lanius collurio*

Now vagrant. Former summer visitor and passage-migrant.

Until the 1920s a widespread summer visitor throughout the county; usually arriving mid-May, occasionally in April, and departing in August, with passage into September or occasionally October. Most common on the coast and levels, scarcer in the west. Disappeared from the east of the county by 1930s, and from the levels at the end of the 1950s. Odd pairs bred on Mendips and Exmoor until 1962. Last breeding record on Quantocks in 1966; it had bred there annually since 1935.

Only five single records in the last 20 years: Ash Priors, September 1967; Curry Moor, 8 June 1968; Charterhouse, 28 May 1977; Brean Down, 14 October 1984; and Porlock Marsh, 25 May 1987.

Lesser Grey Shrike   *Lanius minor*

Vagrant

Two records, both of adults: Meare, 1 June 1977; West Sedge Moor, 21–23 July 1980.

Great Grey Shrike   *Lanius excubitor*

Winter visitor; rare.

About 25 records from 1840 to 1965. All single birds except for two together, Mendips, November/December 1964. In the 21 years to 1986, there have been 36 records, over half on the Mendips, Quantocks and Exmoor, the rest scattered throughout the county; all single birds except for two, Rookham, 13 December 1970. All records between 15 October and 17 April, with the majority from October to December.

Three summer records: Bicknoller, 24 June 1949; Raleigh's Cross, 26 April–9 July 1953; Stolford, 30 May 1961.

Woodchat Shrike   *Lanius senator*

Vagrant.

Three records of single birds: Winscombe (Avon) or Cheddar Wood, about 1860; Bossington, 26/27 May 1926; Creech St Michael, 21–24 May 1974. Of these, the first may not have been within the present county.

Jay   *Garrulus garrulus*

Resident; common. Occasional passage-migrant.

Much persecuted in the last century, but by the early 1900s was common in woodland areas everywhere. Before 1965, flocks of 15–20 were said to be frequent, and 100 were in Loxley Woods, 30 September 1940 (possibly an influx year).

Remains common today, mostly in deciduous woodland; usually reported in pairs or small parties. Light passage noted in some years, April/May and September/October, most noticeably on the coast from Brean to Steart, occasionally inland.

During October 1983 there was a large influx in south-west England, with flocks of several thousand in Devon and Cornwall. In Somerset, small flocks were widespread throughout, with the largest counts of 125 to the west, Stolford, on 12th, and about 100 in ten minutes near Brean Down around the same time.

Magpie   *Pica pica*

Resident; very common. Occasional passage-migrant.

Like the Jay, much persecuted in the nineteenth century. Numbers increased steadily from about 1914, and it is now abundant in many areas on the levels, and common everywhere else except the high tops of Exmoor, where nest sites are less freely available. Outside the breeding season, flocks of up to ten are common, with larger totals usually at roosts; the highest count is 106 at a regular roost in Sea Buckthorn at Berrow, February 1984.

Nutcracker   *Nucifraga caryocatactes*

Vagrant.

Four earlier records, all single birds: Bridgwater, autumn 1805; Cothelstone, late summer 1873; King's Cliff Wood, 4 August 1873; Dunster, August/September 1940.

In the invasion of October 1968, there were at least three and possibly five in Somerset: one at Ilminster on the 1st; one shot at Athelney on the 8th; and others at Ilchester on the 13th, Wootton Courtenay from the 3rd to the 23rd, and Minehead on 27th.

Chough   *Pyrrhocorax pyrrhocorax*

Vagrant. Formerly bred.

Bred on the cliffs west of Minehead until at least 1869. In 1910, three immatures were seen at Bossington Cliffs and at Porlock, in August/September, so may have bred into the early 1900s. Apart from seven together near County Gate in 1878, there have only been twelve other records since, all of single birds, the last being above Bicknoller, 6 October 1984.

Jackdaw   *Corvus monedula*

Resident; very common. Passage-migrant and winter visitor.

Proved breeding in every 10-km square, in a variety of habitats from woods, hedgerow trees and parkland to cliffs, old ruined buildings and suburban chimneys. Sometimes in large colonies in quarries and on cliffs, with at least 150 pairs in Cheddar Gorge. Local on high ground in the west.

Autumn passage has been reported in only four years since 1950, but is probably regular as young birds disperse from breeding areas. Large flights of Jackdaws are noted throughout the year around Cheddar Gorge, as birds feed on the hills and lowland fields by day and return to roost at dusk.

Rook   *Corvus frugilegus*

Resident, passage-migrant and winter visitor; very common.

Although it is still a common bird, there has been a considerable decline from the peak numbers in the 1940s. In 1933/34 there were 30,488 nests in the area covered by the present county, with 46 per cent in elm trees (Tucker, 1935, 1936). The BTO survey in 1975 found 19,047 nests, with 51 per cent in elm (a reduction of 37.5 per cent). Dutch elm disease has subsequently removed virtually all of the elms in Somerset, but several local surveys suggest that numbers of Rooks are similar to 1975, with ash and oak the most frequently used trees (Box, 1988).

Breeds throughout the county, mostly below the 125m contour, but scarce on the levels where most rookeries are on slightly raised ground. Uncommon on the Mendips, Quantocks and Exmoor, but there is a colony of at least 100 nests at Warren Farm, Simonsbath (400m). In 1944, breeding was first noted on electricity pylons on the levels, and in recent years it has occurred there almost annually.

In autumn and winter, feeding flocks are widespread, particularly on stubble fields, including a flock of at least 1500 birds with Jackdaws in a field east of Cheddar Gorge, in December 1985. There is probably some immigration during this time.

Carrion Crow *Corvus corone*

Resident; very common.

Up to the early 1900s, persecution by gamekeepers had made it rare in some areas. Since 1920 numbers have greatly increased, and it is now very common, with flocks up to 150 (occasionally 300) reported annually, mainly during the winter.

During the breeding season very common everywhere, with odd pairs nesting as low as one metre in isolated trees on Exmoor and the levels. First recorded nesting on pylons in 1937; this is now annual. In the late 1950s, nests were found on heaps of driftwood, at Steart and Steart Island. For further details see Parsons (1977).

Hooded Crow *C.c. cornix*
Winter visitor; rare. Now probably only a vagrant.

An irregular visitor, with 14 records November/December 1861–1905. Singly or in pairs, but five together near Cheddar in 1900.

Since 1923 has been recorded 23 times, mostly on the coast and the Blackdowns. Except for one in August, all between 24 October and 25 April; singly or up to three together.

Raven *Corvus corax*

Resident; local.

Bred spasmodically at Cheddar Gorge until 1936, and almost annually on Brean Down 1900–72. Now encountered in both areas in most winters, September–March, with occasional summer records, usually of up to three together. Although a pair inhabited Glastonbury Tor in the 1840s, the only recent breeding on the levels took place at Shapwick in 1958. Now only an infrequent visitor, October–March. First appeared on the Blackdowns in 1971; now present most years, in small numbers, and has bred at least once.

Up to four pairs have bred on the Quantocks since 1912, usually on the cliffs at the northern end, but occasionally in trees inland. There are scattered winter records in most years.

On Exmoor, reduced in the nineteenth century to a few pairs on coastal cliffs between Minehead and Glenthorne. From about 1914 a return was made to inland habitats, and it is now well distributed across the Moor in isolated trees. One or two pairs have occasionally bred in quarries on the Brendons, and on cliffs between Watchet and Blue Anchor.

Large flocks are sometimes seen in the west; usually 15–30, occasionally up to 50. An exceptional gathering of 110 was feeding on dead sheep, Exmoor, 4 March 1978.

Starling   *Sturnus vulgaris*

Resident, winter visitor and passage-migrant; abundant.

Proved breeding in every 10-km square in the county, wherever buildings and trees provide suitable sites, and occasionally on cliffs. Sometimes scarce or absent in higher Exmoor valleys.

Flocking usually begins in late June, with the main influx of migrants arriving from late September to November and leaving in March and early April. Winter visitors originate from the USSR, the Baltic and Low Countries, as well as central and northern Britain. Large communal roosts occur in woods, copses, and reed- and withy-beds, throughout the winter, with some estimates of up to 500,000 on occasion. Migration noted mainly on the coast, September–November in most years, mainly from Brean Down to Stolford, and around Minehead. In hard weather, large movements may occur throughout the county.

Rose-coloured Starling *Sturnus roseus*

Vagrant.

Nine records of single birds, the first four being shot: Taunton, June 1835; Shapwick, July 1850; Axbridge, 1859; Laverton, 29 July 1869; Porlock, 25 July 1945; Porlock Marsh, 14 May 1957; Williton, 5 September 1963; Bridgwater, June 1963; Wootton Courtenay, 2 November, and Dunster, 9 December 1975, the last two probably the same bird.

House Sparrow *Passer domesticus*

Resident; abundant. Probably also winter visitor.

Widespread but almost always associated with human habitation during the breeding season, nesting in any convenient nook or cranny; occasionally nests in bushes. Absent from some upland farms on Exmoor.

Flocks of up to 300, occasionally 500, are found on farmland in autumn and winter.

May also occur as a passage-migrant; flocks of up to 200 have passed over Steep Holm (Avon) in October, but the only Somerset record is a female or immature that flew in from the Channel, at the tip of Brean Down, 10 October 1954. It is probably overlooked.

Tree Sparrow *Passer montanus*

Resident, winter visitor and passage-migrant; very scarce and local.

Bred commonly on the levels, with scattered records from the rest of the county, until 1915; it had almost disappeared by 1925, when it was breeding only near Taunton. Until 1956 only a few isolated breeding records, but then began to return to many areas, particularly the Central and South Levels. In 1971 at least 24 pairs were located, and until 1978 an average of 11 pairs nested. Since then numbers have again fallen, with only about six pairs in 1986.

In the late 1950s came a large increase of winter records, and small flocks were widespread during the next 20 years, with counts occasionally up to 50, exceptionally 200. It has again become much scarcer in recent years, with few parties over ten.

Passage occasionally reported on the coast from Brean to Berrow, sometimes May, usually October, normally in single figures. An exceptional count in 1971, when 135 flew south at Berrow on 24 October.

Chaffinch   *Fringilla coelebs*

Resident, passage-migrant and winter visitor; abundant.

Breeds throughout the county wherever there are trees and bushes; the highest density is in mature deciduous woodland, but also common in gardens, parks and farmland.

The local population is sedentary but is augmented in winter by influxes of continental migrants, predominantly females. In autumn and winter large flocks feed in stubble fields and on rough ground, particularly on the coast, and often with other finches. Very common diurnal migrant in autumn, most conspicuous on the coast, particularly from Brean Down to Stolford and west of Minehead, with occasional movement noted inland. Passage from late September to the end of November, with peak from 19 October to 7 November; heaviest movement usually from daybreak to noon, and mainly down-Channel. Large numbers may be involved, as shown by counts of 3600 an hour, Burnham-on-Sea, 26 October 1961; and 2800 an hour, Berrow, 19 October 1980. Hard-weather movements can occur in December/January.

Brambling   *Fringilla montifringilla*

Winter visitor and passage-migrant; local.

Very irregular in numbers, since largely dependent on the availability of beechmast throughout its wintering range. Most regular on the coast from Brean Down to the Quantocks, especially Steart, where from 1965 to 1976 flocks of up to 300 occurred in most years, occasionally 600; an exceptional total of 2000 on 22 January 1967. Small numbers encountered inland in most years, flocks seldom exceeding 50, though up to 700 have been seen in good years, generally around beech trees. Much scarcer since 1977, with few flocks over 80.

Normally a nocturnal migrant, but is noted in small numbers in daylight on the coast from Brean to Berrow. Rare in September; main passage in October and November. Wintering birds from November to February, with return movement early March to mid-April; occasional stragglers into May, and one singing, Culbone Woods, 22–27 June 1956.

Serin   *Serinus serinus*

Vagrant.

Three records: one shot, Taunton, end of January 1866; male, Brean Down, 8 May 1965; male, Berrow, 21 November 1987.

Greenfinch   *Carduelis chloris*

Resident, passage-migrant and winter visitor; fairly common.

Originally a bird of the woodland edge but is now well distributed, nesting in hedgerows, thickets and gardens. Scarce on high ground, and a summer visitor to some Exmoor valleys, March to October. In autumn and winter, flocks of up to several hundred occur in stubble and rough fields with other finches. Common in gardens and increasingly regular at peanut feeders.

Light passage along the coast, Brean Down to Berrow and west of Minehead, in most years, from late September to mid-November, usually down-Channel.

Goldfinch *Carduelis carduelis*

Resident, summer visitor, winter visitor and passage-migrant; locally common.

Numbers were much reduced in the nineteenth century by birdcatchers, but since 1900 has become a common breeder on low ground throughout. Scarce on high ground, being absent from some Exmoor valleys in certain years.

Flocks start assembling in late summer, feeding on thistles, teasels and other seed-bearing plants. Ringing has shown that a large proportion of the British-bred birds winter in south-west France and northern Spain. Movement is noted in late September to November, mostly on the coast, somtimes inland; the direction is variable. Parties of up to 50, occasionally more, are common in open country during the winter. Spring passage is rarely visible, and the winter flocks disperse during April and May.

Siskin *Carduelis spinus*

Resident; scarce. Passage-migrant and winter visitor; fairly common locally.

An irregular and scarce winter visitor in the early 1900s. Numbers gradually increased, and by the 1970s parties of up to 40 and occasionally 80 occurred throughout the county, especially in alders, larch and birch. Since 1971 has been widespread and common in most winters, in flocks of 100–250 in most years. An exceptional flock of 600 was at Rode, 8 December 1985.

Small numbers of migrants in September and early October on the coast from Brean to Porlock, with the main influx of wintering birds in October/

November. In spring, birds disperse from late March to mid-April, with migrants occasionally into May.

Over the years singing males were sometimes heard in April, and in 1978 and 1979 birds were recorded on the Quantocks and Exmoor in May and June. Breeding first proved in 1979 at Luccombe, where one or two pairs have bred annually since. In 1985 a total of 17 pairs/singing males were present in the summer, on the Quantocks, Exmoor and the Blackdowns. The spread of this species in Britain can be partly attributed to the increase in commercial forestry and the coniferous plantations that blanket many of the upland slopes.

Linnet   *Carduelis cannabina*

Resident, passage-migrant and winter visitor; common.

A widespread resident in lowland areas, particularly on the coast and on the peat-moors. Much lower density on Exmoor and the higher valleys, the local birds moving to lower ground in winter. Has undoubtedly declined over the last 20 years, mostly as a result of the extensive use of herbicides, which have reduced the amount of seed-bearing weeds.

Passage in spring light and variable, usually along the coast in March and April. Much more evident in autumn, from mid-September to November, again on the coast and on rough ground inland. Most pass south-west, others join residents to feed wherever seeds are available, from coastal mudflats to farmland and the peat-moors. Flocks of up to 50 are not unusual, occasionally up to 400.

Twite   *Carduelis flavirostris*

Winter visitor; scarce.

Very rare before 1949; 11 occurred on the Bridgwater Bay salt-marshes in the late nineteenth century, and a female was shot at Wells, 15 February 1905. About 200 have been recorded since, singly or in small parties, occasionally up to 18. Unusually high numbers in the winter of 1984/85, when up to 80 were present. Normally recorded on the coast from Brean to Porlock Marsh, but 15 seen inland, most at Cheddar Reservoir and the rest at six other sites. The majority of records from 19 October to 26 March; one in September and three in April.

Redpoll *Carduelis flammea*

Resident, passage-migrant and winter visitor; local.

From 1888 to 1914, a rare breeder, nesting in at least ten sites across the county. From then to 1947, single breeding records from five sites. Since then has established an annual but fluctuating breeding population in birch and pine woodland on north-east Exmoor, and has bred irregularly on the Quantocks since 1952, and on the Mendips and Blackdowns since 1971.

Autumn passage from August to mid-November, mainly on the coast but occasionally inland. Winter visitors arrive from early October, and are seen throughout the county feeding on alders and birch, often associating with Siskins and other finches. Departure mainly in February/March but flocks will linger into May and occasionally June. Flocks in any season rarely exceed 50.

Mealy Redpoll *C.f. flammea*
Vagrant.

One record: Westhay Moor, 14 February 1960.

Crossbill *Loxia curvirostra*

Irregular visitor. Has bred.

Subject to periodic irruptions, usually in late summer and autumn, some birds remaining for months or even for several years. A few have bred. There were about nine irruptions from 1791 to 1894. After a large influx in 1927, breeding took place at several sites. Since 1964, recorded all years except three; of the rest, five had single records, and 1972 and 1985 were invasion years. Probably bred on Exmoor in 1981 and 1982, and possibly on the Quantocks in 1987 and 1988, and Gare Hill in 1988.

Although recorded in all parts of the county, most are on the Mendips, Quantocks and Exmoor; it has benefited from the conifer plantations, preferring spruce and larch. Usually in small parties up to 10, occasionally up to 70, and an exceptional flock of at least 150, Stock Hill, 30 July 1972.

Several have been reported flying south in October/November, all on the coast between Berrow and Steart.

Scarlet Rosefinch   *Carpodacus erythrinus*

Vagrant.

Three records: female or young male, Cheddar Reservoir, 5 October 1952; female or immature, Brean Down, 14–18 October 1977; a singing male, Westhay Moor, 1/2 June 1988.

Bullfinch   *Pyrrhula pyrrhula*

Resident and perhaps winter visitor; fairly common.

Widespread throughout the county, breeding wherever suitable dense cover occurs. In spring, its liking for buds makes it unpopular with fruitgrowers and gardeners, and it has suffered persecution in the past. Feeds on a succession of seed-bearing plants through the year, even on Exmoor, where it likes ling and heather seeds. Usually in pairs or family parties, but at favoured feeding sites up to ten or more may occur.

Hawfinch   *Coccothraustes coccothraustes*

Resident (?) and irregular winter visitor; local and rare.

Before 1880 a rare winter visitor, though bred at Shepton Mallet, 1859. Increased from 1880 to 1925, breeding in at least six separate localities across the county. Recorded almost annually since, with occasional nesting in at least 12 places, the most recent near Frome in 1968. It is possible that breeding is more regular, but the elusiveness of this species makes confirmation difficult.

Most records are between March and September, singly or in pairs; exceptionally six, Westhay Heath, 30 June 1986.

Winter records are irregular, and usually of one or two birds in gardens or hedgerows.

Dark-eyed Junco   *Junco hyemalis*

Vagrant.

One record: a male, Langford Budville, 21 May 1983.

Lapland Bunting   *Calcarius lapponicus*

Autumn and winter visitor; rare.

First recorded at Steart, 26/27 February 1956, and has been reported in 19 out of the last 30 years. Mostly on the coast between Brean Down and Steart, and from Porlock Marsh in 1957, and Dunster Beach in 1980. There have been eight inland records of single birds, all since 1977; three at Cheddar Reservoir, one at Wimbleball and the rest on the Central and South Levels.

Apart from three in September (earliest, 25th), and eight in March (latest, 25th), the rest fall between 2 October and 25 February. Of about 88 recorded, there were parties of three on two occasions, and four twice. All other records were of one or two birds, apart from exceptional numbers on Wall Common, 8 January to 12 February 1978, which reached a peak of 14 on the 14th.

Snow Bunting   *Plectrophenax nivalis*

Winter visitor and passage-migrant; scarce and local.

Recorded since the early nineteenth century, and occurs almost annually. Most records on the coast from Brean Down to Stolford and Dunster to Porlock. Occasional inland, mainly on Exmoor, and at Cheddar and Sutton Bingham Reservoirs.

Three September records (earliest on 2nd) before the main passage and arrival from mid-October, when most are passing through. Peak numbers mid-November to February; most reports are of one or two birds, occasionally up to eight, exceptionally 40, the larger numbers are usually between Brean Down and Steart.

Main departure in February, scarcer in March, and about 20 in April (latest 19th), including a flock of 14.

Yellowhammer *Emeriza citrinella*

Resident and passage-migrant; locally common.

Thought to have decreased as a breeding species since 1900, but is still well distributed across the county. The *Breeding Atlas* shows it present in every 10-km square in the county, with breeding proved in most. However, the distribution is patchy, with pairs scattered on the Mendips, along the Poldens and on Ham Hill, and scarce or absent on the levels between. Common in the east, particularly south of Wincanton, and very common along hedgerows around Langport, Ilminster and Crewkerne. Common on the Blackdowns and on lower slopes of the Quantocks and Exmoor, and especially on the Brendons, but rare in high moorland combes. A few pairs breed along the coast from Brean Down to Watchet and west of Minehead.

Passage occasionally noted on the coast between Brean and Stolford in autumn, and more frequently Minehead to Porlock, in October. In autumn, birds leave the higher ground and form flocks, often with finches, on agricultural land and rougher coastal areas. Most flocks are under 40, but occasionally up to 150.

Cirl Bunting *Emberiza cirlus*

Resident; now rare.

First recorded in 1805 on the Poldens, and from the late nineteenth century until the 1960s its distribution seems to have been fairly stable. It was locally common on the lower slopes of the Mendips from Axbridge to Wells; and from Burnham-on-Sea inland to Brent Knoll; more local on the Poldens, around Glastonbury, and on the peat-moors. Locally common from North Wootton to Castle Cary; and well distributed across the area bounded by Somerton, Yeovil, Crewkerne, Ilminster and Langport, excluding the South Levels. Local in West Sedge Moor/Taunton area, and along the coast from Brean Down to Porlock Weir; occasional records from other areas.

Little change until the mid-1960s, when it disappeared from the east of the county, lingering at North Wootton until 1969. By 1973 the population was estimated at 30–40 pairs, with concentrations on south-facing slopes on the Mendips, and around Langport and Porlock. The decline has continued. The BTO Survey in 1982 indicated a population of 19 pairs at 12 sites, but in 1987 only five singing males/pairs could be located, and none in their former stronghold between Wells and Cheddar. The national decline is well documented and is reflected in Somerset; however, the unpredictable behaviour of this species makes it difficult to find.

For breeding, the preferred habitat is low-lying agricultural land, parkland or large gardens, usually small areas enclosed by mature hedgerows with trees, particularly elms in the past. With the loss of our elm trees due to disease, the most favoured sites are now gardens with ornamental conifers.

Winter records are few, and are usually close to breeding haunts, especially in the Langport area, and formerly Cheddar.

Ortolan Bunting   *Emberiza hortulana*

Vagrant.

Seven records of single birds: Brean Down, 10 September 1961, and 18 August 1971; Brue Estuary, 6 September 1981; Sutton Bingham Reservoir, 17 September 1983; Draycott, 31 August 1986; Brean Down, 5 September 1986. A male at Cheddar Reservoir, 25 April 1987, is the only spring record.

Little Bunting   *Emberiza pusilla*

Vagrant.

One record: one trapped at Nether Stowey, 19 February 1976.

Yellow-breasted Bunting   *Emberiza aureola*

Vagrant.

One record: immature, Berrow, 13 September 1980.

Reed Bunting *Emberiza schoeniclus*

Resident, passage-migrant and winter visitor; locally common.

Breeds throughout, in reed-beds and rank waterside vegetation. Most common on the levels, less well distributed on reservoirs, ponds and rivers. Rare in the south and east due to lack of habitat. Regularly breeds well away from water in bracken and gorse on the Mendips and Blackdowns and sometimes on Exmoor, and even in young conifer plantation scrub near Gare Hill.

In winter, small flocks associate with finches in reeds, sea-aster beds, and stands of reed-mace. In hard weather will even venture into town gardens and parks. Most flocks are of up to 20, occasionally up to 100 on the coast. A roost at Crewkerne during October and November 1985 was used by more than 500 birds; a few were residents but most were migrants passing through (Parsons, 1985). On the coast, passage from September to November, and small numbers occasionally noted in March.

Corn Bunting   *Miliaria calandra*

Resident; scarce and local.

Bred at many places across the county before 1960 but always rather local and irregular. Shows a marked preference for arable farms and cornfields with hedges, post-and-wire fences and electricity pylons, which are used as song-posts. The birds are only present while such fields exist, and then move on. Has bred regularly on Mendips: usually two to six pairs around Yoxter, but 12 singing birds present at Green Ore in 1986 were only there for one year. Between 1960 and 1973, up to 13 pairs on Somerton Moor, and eight pairs on West Sedge Moor. Has since disappeared at the first site and only one or two persist at the second. From 1971 to 1974, up to 20 singing males in the South Petherton/Shepton Beauchamp area, but few since. At Weston-zoyland Airfield, up to eight singing males/pairs regularly recorded since 1964, and in 1980/81 12 pairs were in the Milborne Wick area. Since 1985, 12–15 pairs have been found at the RNAS, Yeovilton. Up to five pairs occasionally at other sites, but they seldom persist. Rare west of Taunton.

   In winter, occasional on the coast from Brean to Steart, and in mixed finch flocks inland; total numbers rarely exceed ten.

Appendix

(Records Not Accepted in the Specific List)

(A) SPECIES RECORDED IN SOUTH AVON BEFORE THE BOUNDARY CHANGES

The following were recorded before 1974 within the 'old' county of Somerset but have not yet been seen in the 'new' county:

Pied-billed Grebe *Podilymbus podiceps*
Bridled Tern *Sterna anaethetus*
Sooty Tern *Sterna fuscata*
Lesser Yellowlegs *Tringa flavipes*
Hawk Owl *Surnia ulula*
Arctic Warbler *Phylloscopus borealis*
Two-barred Crossbill *Loxia leucoptera*

One species, the Killdeer *Charadrius vociferus*, occurred in south Avon in 1976; this was after the division of the counties, but before *RSB* stopped publishing records for south Avon.

(B) RECORDS PREVIOUSLY ACCEPTED BUT NOW BEING RECONSIDERED

Bonaparte's Gull   *Larus philadelphia*

Immature, Cheddar Reservoir, 28 August 1968. Doubts have been cast on this record, which is currently being reviewed.

(C) RECORDS STILL UNDER CONSIDERATION AT TIME OF GOING TO PRESS

The following recent records are still being considered by the *British Birds* Rarities Committee:

Little Shearwater   *Puffinus assimilis*

One, off Hinkley Point, 3 September 1988

Night Heron   *Nycticorax nycticorax*

An immature sporting four colour rings, Orthery Moor area, from mid-February to at least April 1988, now traced as an escapee from Edinburgh Zoo.

American Wigeon   *Anas americana*

A male, Wimbleball Reservoir, 28 December 1987 till 24 March 1988 this was probably the same bird of the 1986/87 winter. A female was claimed at the same site in early 1988.

Ring-necked Duck   *Aythya collaris*

A female at Cheddar Reservoir, 17–25 November 1987, and probably same at Hawkridge Reservoir, 6 December; two males there, 2–12 December; all three at Ashford Reservoir, 19 December; the female there on 26th, and a male at Hawkridge the same day.

Marbled Teal   *Marmaronetta angustirostris*

One at Cheddar Reservoir, from 22 September to 28 October 1984. If accepted as being a vagrant, this will be the first British record.

Least Sandpiper   *Calidris minutilla*

One, Steart, 16 August 1988.

Terek Sandpiper   *Xenus cinereus*

One, Porlock Marsh, 28 May 1987. Two, Steart, 15 August 1988.

Laughing Gull *Larus atricilla*

A second-winter, Parrett Estuary, 2 September 1988.

Ring-billed Gull *Larus delawarensis*

A second-year, Durleigh Reservoir, 16 October 1987. Only eight previous records, all at Sutton Bingham Reservoir.

Alpine Swift *Apus melba*

Single birds, Yeovil, 17 March, and Westonzoyland, 12 June 1988.

Red-breasted Flycatcher *Ficedula parva*

A record of one at Steart, 21 August 1978, has only recently been reported. We wait for further details before accepting what will be a first for the county.

Bibliography

There have been a number of different works of importance that dealt with the birds of the whole county, including what is now south Avon.

The earliest is Cecil Smith's *The Birds of Somersetshire* (London, 1869). Like many Victorian county ornithologies, this contains much information that is of general rather than county interest, but it is all that we have for this early period, other than for a few notes in *The Zoologist* and other periodicals. There is a good deal of Somerset information in D'Urban and Mathew's *Birds of Devon* (London, 1892); more indeed for some species than in Mathew's separate *Revised List of the Birds of Somerset*, published in the *Proceedings of the Somerset Archaeological and Natural History Society* for 1893. More important was the Reverend F.L. Blathwayt's article on birds in Volume I of the *Victoria County History of Somerset*, written in 1901 and published in 1906. Stanley Lewis's *The Breeding Birds of Somerset and their Eggs* (Ilfracombe, 1955) is a strangely archaic work for its date. Its author was a passionate egg-collector of the old school, but also an excellent field naturalist; his collections are mostly in the City Museum at Bristol.

The most recent work is Palmer and Ballance's *The Birds of Somerset* (London, 1968), a book of a similar kind to the present one. This summarised records up to 1965 (some for 1966). We have depended heavily on this for earlier records, and have consulted their original notes in order to seperate south Avon and Somerset records. For a full bibliography of older articles, see pp. 189 to 193 of their work.

Almost all our records are drawn from *The Report on Somerset Birds*. This was published at intervals as a typescript from 1911 to 1923 by the Ornithological Section of the Somerset Archaeological and Natural History Society; from 1924 it has appeared annually, so it has one of the longest runs of any English county bird report. In 1974 the Section split from the parent body and formed the Somerset Ornithological Society, but this produced no change in the form of the *Report*. Until 1976, this included notes on the birds of south Avon. It was printed from 1924 to 1977; from 1978 to 1984 it appeared as a typescript (though within the same covers); it is now again printed. From 1924 to 1983 records were analysed under seven Districts (of which 'I' was roughly identical to south Avon and was therefore dropped in 1977); from 1984 a slightly different division has been used, based on the 1:25,000 grid squares.

Some other recent material is contained in two news-sheets published by the Society: *Goldeneye* and the more recent *Bird Notes*.

The area of south Avon has been covered since 1974 by the *Avon Bird Report*; up to 1982 this was published in the *Proceedings of the Bristol Naturalists' Society*, but in 1983 it became a separate publication produced by the Avon Ornithological Group, a body set up solely for that purpose.

Many Exmoor records are collected and published by the Exmoor Natural History Society, which also submits them for the county *Report*. On the westward side, *The Report of the Devon Birdwatching and Preservation Society* (1928) has often contained Exmoor material that is relevant to Somerset, and it did for a time in the 1930s and 1940s publish regular material on west Somerset.

We have made use of a number of national surveys carried out for the British Trust for Ornithology and other bodies, and published in *Bird Study* or *British Birds*. We have been greatly helped in non-passerines by the appearance of the first four volumes of the *Handbook of the Birds of Europe, the Middle East and North Africa (The Birds of the Western Palearctic)* (Cramp, Simmons *et al.*, Oxford 1977).

OTHER SOURCES

We here list a number of other books and papers which we have used; not all are directly cited in the text. They include all papers which have been published in *The Report on Somerset Birds* since 1966.

ALLEN, N.V., *The Birds of Exmoor*. (2nd ed.). Williton, 1976.
ALLEN, N.V., Ring Ouzel in Exmoor National Park. *RSB*. 83–6, 1984.
ATKINSON-WILLES, G.L.(ed.), *Wildfowl in Great Britain*. London, 1963.

BALLANCE, D.K., The duck decoys of Somerset. *RSB.* 55–8, 1971.

BALLANCE, D.K., List of the birds of Somerset and South Avon. *RSB.* 68–75, 1977.

BALLANCE, D.K., Addenda and Corrigenda to this. *RSB.* 63–4, 1978.

BERRY, R., and BIBBY, C.J., A Breeding study of Nightjars. *Brit. Birds.* 74: 161–9, 1981.

BOX, T.A., A report on rookery surveys in the Cheddar area O.S. ST45. *Bird Notes* 4: 2–7, 1988.

CLARK, N., *The ecology of Dunlin wintering on the Severn Estuary,* 1983. D.Phil. thesis, University of Edinburgh, 1983.

CLARK, N., Surge in Severn studies. *BTO News.* 151, 1987.

DAVIS, S., and JARMAN, R.(eds.), *Exmoor Moorland Ornithological Survey,* 1978. A report prepared for the RSPB and the STNC and privately circulated.

DUNNING, R.W., Not one Sparrow. . . . *RSB.* 64–5, 1976.

ELEY, J.T., Hoopoes breeding in Avon. *Bristol Ornithology* 11: 35–6, 1978.

EXMOOR NATURAL HISTORY SOCIETY, *The Flora and Fauna of the Exmoor National Park.* Minehead, 1988.

FERNS, P.N., GREEN, G.H., and ROUND, P.D., Significance of the Somerset and Gwent Levels in Britain as feeding areas for migrant Whimbrels, *Numenius phaeopus. Biological Conservation* 16: 1: 7–22, 1979.

FOX, A.D., and ASPINALL, S.J., Pomarine Skuas in Britain and Ireland in autumn 1985. *Brit. Birds* 80: 404–421, 1987.

HALL, K., and GOVETT, J., *Where to watch birds in Somerset, Avon, Gloucester and Wiltshire.* London.

HOLLOM, P.A.D., Changes in numbers of Swallows' and House Martins' nests in Somerset over 50-year period. *Brit. Birds* 78: 240, 1985.

HOPKIN, P., A 'flight' of seabirds in September 1983. *Bristol Ornithology* 18: 117–23. 1985.

HUTCHINSON, C.D., and NEATH, B., Little Gulls in Britain and Ireland. *Brit. Birds* 71: 563–81, 1978.

KING, B., Spring influx of Scandinavian Lesser Black-backed Gulls in north Somerset. *Bristol Ornithology* 5: 205–6, 1972.

MORLEY, J.V., The moult migration of Shelduck from Bridgwater Bay. *Brit. Birds* 59: 141–7, 1966.

MORLEY, J.V., Tidal immersion of *Spartina* Marsh at Bridgwater Bay, Somerset. *J.Ecol.* 61: 383–6, 1973.

MORLEY, J.V., *The Birds of Bridgwater Bay*. Taunton. A report for the NCC. (This has a full bibliography of papers on the area), 1986.

MORLEY, J.V., and COOK, R.S., Moult migration at Bridgwater Bay and migration routes from South-west and Southern England. *Brit. Birds* 63: 2, 1970.

PARSONS, A.J., The breeding birds of the parish of Crewkerne. *RSB*. 55–6, 60, 1975.

PARSONS, A.J., The 1975 Rookery Census. *id.*: 57–9 (with Addenda and Corrigenda in *RSB* 1976: 63–4), 1975.

PARSONS A.J.,1977. The Carrion Crow in the old county of Somerset. *RSB*. 76–80.

PARSONS A.J., A cold-weather movement of Chaffinches at Crewkerne. *RSB*: 72–5, 1985.

PARSONS A.J., Examination of a Reed Bunting roost at Millwater, Crewkerne. *RSB*: 75–8, 1985.

PARSONS A.J., Autumn and winter movements of thrushes in Somerset. *RSB*: 77–84, 1986.

RABBITTS, B. and VINICOMBE, K.E., Wallcreeper wintering in Somerset. *Bristol Ornithology* 11: 17–20, 1978.

ROGERS, M.J., Ruddy Shelducks in Britain in 1965–79. *Brit. Birds* 75: 446–55, 1982.

ROBBINS, M., Ornithological studies at Hinkley Point. *RSB*: 79–83, 1985.

ROUND, P.D., *An Ornithological Study of the Somerset Levels, 1976–77*. Bristol and Sandy. A report for the Wessex Water Authority and the RSPB, 1978.

SLADE, B.E., Hoopoes breeding in Somerset. *Bristol Ornithology* 11: 21–2, 1978.

SLADE, B.E., The birds of Berrow 1973 to 1980. *id.* 14: 119–30, 1981.

SLADE, B.E., and McGEOCH, J.A., The spring passage of the Whimbrel (*Numenius phaeopus*) in Somerset, with particular reference to the Steart Island roost. *RSB*: 65–8. (This cites various papers), 1979.

SOMERSET TRUST FOR NATURE CONSERVATION (pubs.), *Somerset brick-pits: their future*. A Report prepared by the Sedgemoor Committee of the STNC, 1977.

SPENCER, R. *et al.*, Rare breeding birds in the United Kingdom in 1985. *Brit. Birds* 81: 99–125, 1988.

STORER, B., *The Natural History of the Somerset Levels.* Revised edition. Wimborne, 1985.

SUTER, G., The 1976 Nightingale Census. *RSB*. 61–3, 1976.

TUCKER, B.W., The Rookeries of Somerset. *Proc. Som. Arch. and Nat. Hist. Soc.* XXXI: 149–240, 1935.

TUCKER, B.W., The Rookeries of Somerset. *id*. XXXII: 216, 1936.

WEAVER, D.J., MURFITT, R.C., and CHOWN, D.J., A Survey of the birds of the Somerset Moors, 1982–83, and the effects of drainage. *RSB*:78–85, 1983.

Organisations for the Recording and Conservation of Birds in Somerset

THE SOMERSET ORNITHOLOGICAL SOCIETY was founded only in 1974, by members who had seceded from the Ornithological Section of the Somerset Archaeological and Natural History Society; this had been founded in 1910, and still exists, but the responsibility for producing the annual *Report on Somerset Birds* devolved upon the SOS, which also holds indoor and field meetings.

SOS Membership Secretary, 1988–9: Miss E.M. Seaman, 2 Cothelstone Close, Durleigh, Bridgwater, Somerset (phone Bridgwater 451368).

Recorder: B. Rabbitts, Flat 3, 17 The Esplanade, Burnham-on-Sea, Somerset, TA8 1BG (tel: Burnham-on-Sea 789068).

THE SOMERSET TRUST FOR NATURE CONSERVATION was founded in 1964. It plays a leading part in all matters relating to conservation of wildlife within the county. It owns or manages a number of reserves, some of which are of importance for birds.

Address: Fyne Court, Broomfield, Bridgwater (tel: Kingston St Mary 587).

THE MID-SOMERSET NATURALIST SOCIETY was founded in 1949. Its ornithological interests centre on the birds of the Bridgwater area, and especially the clay-pits. It publishes a thrice-yearly news letter, and holds field and lecture meetings.

Secretary: C.F.S. Avent, 22 Provident Place, Bridgwater, Somerset TA6 7DT (tel: Bridgwater 459859).

THE YEOVIL AND DISTRICT NATURAL HISTORY SOCIETY was founded in 1962. It holds field meetings and monthly lecture meetings (from September to April).

Secretary: J.G. Keylock, Sunnyside, East Street, Crewkerne, Somerset TA18 7AQ.

THE EXMOOR NATURAL HISTORY SOCIETY was founded in 1974. It is concerned with all branches of natural history in the west of the county and publishes the annual *Exmoor Naturalist*. It also contributes members' records to the *Report on Somerset Birds*.

Secretary: Miss C.J. Giddens, The Alcombe Bookshop, Minehead, Somerset. (tel: Minehead 3425).

THE ROYAL SOCIETY FOR THE PROTECTION OF BIRDS manages the West Sedge Moor reserve and is involved in conservation, research and planning, especially on the levels.

Addresses: The Lodge, Sandy, Beds.

South-west Regional Office: 10 Richmond Road, Exeter, Devon.

There are several Somerset local membership groups, details of which can be obtained from Sandy or Exeter.

THE NATURE CONSERVANCY COUNCIL has been since 1954 responsible for the National Nature Reserve in Bridgwater Bay, where it maintains a warden. None of the other NNR's in Somerset were selected for ornithological reasons but Shapwick Heath attracts breeding Nightingales, Nightjars and Water Rails, while the two Mendip reserves, Rodney Stoke and Ebbor Gorge, both support good populations of typical woodland birds.

The Sites of Special Scientific Interest notified by NCC which are of greatest importance for birds are those on the levels, where widely publicised efforts have been made to retain traditional farming practices for the benefit of both breeding and wintering wildfowl and waders, and of species such as

Yellow Wagtail, Whinchat and Sedge Warbler. In many cases the status quo has only been maintained by management agreements with the farmers concerned. It is intended that in due course further NNR's will be established in this part of the county, extending the work of the RSPB in its West Sedge Moor reserve, a 335ha area of grazing marsh, bought with grant aid from the NCC.

A variety of sites, embracing a range of habitats in the county, have been notified as SSSI's each making a contribution to the conservation of the county's birds. Included amongst these are a number of ancient deciduous woodlands frequented by woodpeckers, Pied Flycatcher, Redstart, Wood Warbler and Nuthatch. The NCC has grant aided the purchase of some of these by the STNC, RSPB and the National Trust, and worked closely with them to establish a series of nature reserves throughout the county.

Address: Roughmoor, Bishop's Hull, Taunton, Somerset TA1 5AA. Tel: Taunton 83211.

SOMERSET

E EAST SOMERSET   S SOUTH SOMERSET
N NORTH SOMERSET SW SOUTH WEST SOMERSET
C CENTRAL SOMERSET W WEST SOMERSET

ALTITUDE

305m 152m 76m

WILTSHIRE

DORSET

AVON

DEVON

BRISTOL CHANNEL

E

SW

N

C

S

Orchardleigh lake
Frome
Shepton Mallet
Bruton
Castle Cary
Wincanton
Wells
Glastonbury
Yeovil
Sutton Bingham res.
Cheddar res.
Westhay Moor
Shapwick Heath
Street
Somerton
Langport
Crewkerne
Tealham Moor
King's Sedge Moor
Burnham-on-Sea
Bridgwater
Huntworth
West Sedge Moor
Ilminster
Chard res.
Chard
Brean Down
Parrett est.
Steart
Chilton
Trinity
Durleigh res.
Taunton
Low Ham res.
Wellington
Watchet
Minehead
Porlock

10km

Gazetteer of Place Names

This is a list of all place names given in the text, apart from large areas and rivers. To find the approximate location of a place, consult the miniture grid of 10-km squares in the bottom left-hand corner of the county Map (pp.00). The references are four-figure, and are preceeded by ST unless stated. Places not named on the latest edition of the OS 1:50,000 map are marked with*.

Alfred's Tower	7435	Bagborough	1633
Alderman's Barrow	SS8342	Bathpool	2526
Alford	6032	Beer	4031
Aller Moor (Aller)	3828	Berkley	8049
Aller Moor (Wedmore)	4345	Berrow	2952
Aller's Wood	SS9226	Bicknoller	1139
Ammerdown	7152	Billbrook	0241
Ash	4720	Bin Combe	1739
Ash Priors	1529	Bishop's Lydeard	1629
Asham Wood	7045	Black Down	4757
Ashcott	4337	Blackford Moor	3948
Ashford Reservoir	2338	Blagdon Hill	2118
Ashington	5621	Blue Anchor	0243
Athelney	3428	Bossington	SS8947
Axbridge	4544	Brean	2955
Axe Estuary	3058	Brean Down	2959
		Brent Knoll	3350
Badgworth	3952	Bridgetown	SS9233
Badgworthy	SS7945	Bridgwater	2937

Bristol Plain Farm	5051	Clatworthy Reservoir	0431
Brompton Regis	SS9531	Cock's Bridge	3616*
Brue Estuary	3047	Cockercombe	1736
Bruton	6835	Cogley Wood	7035
Bruton Forest	7439	Coleford	6849
Buckland Dinham	7551	Combwich	2542
Burchess Hill	1220	Compton Castle	6425
Burcott	5245	Copley Woods	5031
Burnham-on-Sea	3049	Coppleham Cross	SS9234
Burrow Bridge	3531	Corton Ridge	6223
Burtle	4043	Cothelstone	1831
Burton Pynsent	3724	County Gate	SS7948
Butleigh	5233	Creech Hill	6636
Butleigh Moor	4434	Creech St Michael	2725
Butleigh Wood	5033	Crewkerne	4409
Butt Moor	5335	Cricket St Thomas	3708
		Crook Peak	3855
Callow Hill	4455	Crowcombe	1436
Camel Hill	5825	Crowcombe Park Gate	1537
Canada Farm	4140	Croydon Hill	SS9740
Cannington	2539	Culbone	SS8448
Castle Cary	6332	Culbone Hill	SS8247
Castle Neroche	2615	Culver Cliff	SS9647*
Catcott	3939	Curry Moor	3227
Catcott Heath	4041	Curry Rivel	3925
Chains, The	SS7342		
Chains Barrow	SS7341	Dinder	5744
Chantry	7146	Dinnington	4012
Chard	3208	Dipford	2021
Chard Reservoir	3309	Dolebury Warren (Avon)	4558
Charlinch	3208	Doniford	0843
Charterhouse	5055	Doulting	6443
Cheddar	4553	Downside (Holcombe)	6550
Cheddar Clay-Pits	4352	Downside (S. Mallet)	6244
Cheddar Gorge	4754	Drake's Lake	1421
Cheddar Reservoir	4454	Draycott	4750
Cheddon Fitzpaine	2427	Drayton	4024
Chelm's Combe Quarry	4654*	Dulverton	SS9128
Chetsford	SS8542	Dunball	3040
Chillington	3811	Dunkery Beacon/Hill	SS8741
Chilton Moor	3742	Dunster	SS9843
Chilton Trinity	2939	Dunster Beach/Hawen	SS9945

Dunwear	3236	Ham(don) Hill	4716
Durleigh Reservoir	2736	Hardington	7452
		Hardington Mandeville	5111
Eaker Hill	5652	Hartford Woods	SS9529
East Chinnock	4915	Hatch Beauchamp	3020
East Coker	5313	Hawkcombe	SS8745
East Horrington	5846	Hawkridge Reservoir	2036
East Huntspill	3444	Hay Moor	3126
East Lyng	3328	Hayes Wood	SS8533
East Quantoxhead	1343	Heathpoult Cross	SS9436
Edithmead	3249	Hele Manor	SS9224
Ember Combe	SS8541	Helland Hill	3224
Emborough Pond	6150	Hestercombe	2428
Enmore	2335	Highbridge	3247
Exe Head	SS7541	Hinkley Point	2146
Exebridge	SS9324	Hinton St George	4112
Exford	SS8538	Hoar Oak	SS7443
Exford Common	SS8540	Hodder's Combe	1440
		Holcombe	6749
Farleigh Hungerford	8057	Holford	1541
Fiddington	2140	Holford Combe	1540
Fitzhead	1228	Holnicote	SS9146
Fivehead	3523	Horner	SS8845
Frome	7747	Hort Bridge	3415*
Fry's Hill	4355	Huntspill	3145
		Huntworth	3134
Gare Hill	7840	Hurlestone Point	SS8949
Glastonbury	5039		
Glenthorne (Devon)	7949	Ilchester	5223
Godney	4842	Ilminster	3514
Godney Moor	4843	Ilton	3517
Gold Corner	3643	Isle Abbotts	3520
Great Breach Wood	5032	Isle Brewers	3621
Green Ore	5750	Ivystone, The	SS8348
Greenaleigh Point	SS9548		
Greylake	3934	Kennard Moor	5236
		Key Bridge	5513*
Haddon Hill	SS9728	Kilve	1543
Halswell Park	2533	King's Brompton Common	0133*
Ham	2825	King's Cliff Wood	2531
Ham Wall	4640*	King's Moor	4823
Hambridge	3921	King's Sedge Moor	4233

Kingsbury Moor	4421*	Mells	7249
Kingsfield	3706*	Mells Park	7148
Kingston St Mary	2229	Middlezoy	3732
Kinsford Gate	SS7436	Midelney	4025
Knowle Hill	SS9643	Midsomer Norton (Avon)	6654
		Milborne Port	6718
Landacre Bridge	SS8136	Milborne Wick	6620
Lang Moor	3535	Millwater	4310*
Langford Budville	1122	Milverton	1125
Langford Heathfield	1023	Minehead	SS9746
Langport	4226	Montacute	4916
Laverton	7753	Moorhouse	5234
Leigh Reservoir	1917	Mount Fancy	2526
Leigh Woods	1917*	Muchelney	4224
Ley Hill	SS8844		
Lilstock	1744	Nether Stowey	1939
Litton Reservoir	5955	Nettlebridge	6448
Lodge Hill	6431	Nettlecombe	0537
Long Load	4623	New Plantation	5010
Long Sutton	4725	North Curry	3125
Longleat Park (Wilts.)	8043	North Hill	SS9447
Lopen	4214	North Moor (Aller)	3930
Loxley Woods	4037	North Moor (Godney)	4743
Luccombe	SS9144	North Newton	3030
Lucott Moor	SS8543	North Petherton	2933
Luxhay Reservoir	2017	North Wootton	5641
Lydeard House	1729*	Norton Fitzwarren	1926
Lydford	5731	Norton St Philip	7755
Lympsham	3354	Norton-sub-Hamdon	4717
Lynch	SS9047	Nunney	7345
Lyng	3228	Nyland	4550
Lyng Hitchings	3229	Nynehead	1322
Lype Hill	SS9537		
		Oare	SS8047
Maesbury Castle	6047	Oareford	SS8146
Maiden Bradley (Wilts.)	8038	Odcombe	5015
Mansmead Wood	6031*	Orchard Portman	2421
Mark	3847	Orchardleigh	7750
Marston Bigot	7544	Othery	3831
Marston Park	7644	Otterford	2214
Martock	4619	Otterhampton	2443
Meare	4541	Otterhead	2213

Park End	1923	Shapwick	4138
Pawlett	3042	Shapwick Heath	4340
Pen Wood	5109	Sharpham	4637
Pendomer	5210	Shepton Beauchamp	4017
Penselwood	7531	Shepton Mallet	6243
Penzoy Farm	3335	Shipham	4457
Pinkworthy Pond	SS7242	Shute Shelve	4255
Polsham	5142	Simonsbath	SS7739
Poole	1522	Somerset Court Wood	3449
Porlock	SS8846	Somerton	4928
Porlock Marsh	SS8747	Somerton Erleigh	5028*
Porlock Weir	SS8649	Somerton Moor	4631
Postlebury Wood	7443	South Brewham	7236
Priddy	5251	South Moor	3433
Priddy Mineries/Pools	5451	South Petherton	4316
Prior's Park	2116	Southlake Moor	3630
Purchase Copse	4139*	Spaxton	2237
Puriton	3241	Spring Grove	1024
Pylle	6138	Staple Hill	2615
		Staplegrove	2126
Quantock Combe	1737	Stapleton Mead	4422
Quantoxhead	1142	Steart	2745
Queen's Sedge Moor	5341	Steart Island	2948
		Steart Point	2847
Raleigh's Cross	0434	Steep Holm (Avon)	2260
Rams Combe	1637	Sticklepath	0436
Redlynch Park	7032	Stock Hill	5551
Roadwater	0338	Stoford	5613
Roddenbury Hill	7943	Stogursey	2042
Rode	8053	Stoke Moor	4648
Rodney Stoke	4849	Stoke St Gregory	3427
Rookham	4348	Stoke-sub-Hamdon	4717
Rowberrow Warren	4657	Stolford	2245
		Stourhead (Wilts.)	7633
St Audries	1142	Stratton-on-the-Fosse	6550
Sampford Arundel	1018	Street	4836
Sampford Point	1116	Sutton Bingham Reservoir	5511
Sandhill Farm	0241	Sweetworthy	SS8842
Sandhill Park	1629*	Swell Wood	3623
Screech Owl	3135*		
Seavington St Mary	3914	Tadham Moor	4244
Selworthy	SS9246	Tarr Steps	SS8632

Taunton	2325	West Sedge Moor	3626
Tealham Moor	3945	Westbury Moor	4847
Templecombe	7022	Westford	1220
Three Bridges	1722	Westhay	4342
Timberscombe	SS9542	Westhay Heath	4241
Tonedale	1221	Westhay Moor	4544
Treborough	0136	Westonzoyland	3534
Torweston	0940	Wet Moor	4524
		Wheddon Cross	SS9238
Vobster	7049	White Ball	0919
		Whitelackington	3715
Wall Common	2545	Will's Neck	1635
Walrow	3447	Wilmersham Common	SS8642
Walton Moor	4633*	Wimbleball Res./Wood	SS9730
Warren Farm	SS7940	Wincanton	7128
Warren Point	SS9846	Windsor Hill	6145
Washams Wood	4025*	Winscombe (Avon)	4257
Watchet	0743	Winsford	SS9035
Waterrow	0525	Witch Lodge	2519
Wavering Down	4055	Witcombe	4822
Wayford	4006	Witcombe Bottom	4823
Webber's Post	SS9043	Witham Friary	7440
Wedmore	347	Witham Park	7639
Weir Water	SS8345	Withiel Florey	SS9833
Wellington	1320	Withypool	SS8435
Wells	5445	Wiveliscombe	0827
Wembdon	2837	Wookey	5145
West Bagborough	1633	Wootton Courtenay	SS9343
West Chinnock	4615		
West Horrington	5747	Yeovil	5516
West Hill Wood	SS9729	Yeovilton	5422
West Huntspill	3046	Yoxter	5134
West Moor	4121		

Index

Vernacular names are indexed under the last word. Scientific names are indexed under the generic name and are shown in italics. Numbers refer to the main entry for each species. The index does not include references to birds in the first four chapters. For an index to the principal localities see the Gazetteer.